# Demand and Supply functions for Export of Agr. Commodities from India

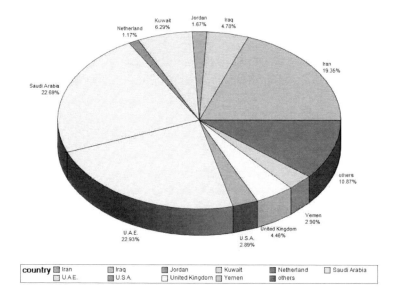

**Figure 4.18 : Destination of India's Basmati Rice Exports (2011)**

Shailza Singh
Latika Sharma
S. S. Burark

# Demand and Supply functions for Export of Agr. Commodities from India

LAP LAMBERT Academic Publishing

Publisher:
LAP LAMBERT Academic Publishing
is a trademark of
International Book Market Service Ltd., member of OmniScriptum Publishing Group
17 Meldrum Street, Beau Bassin 71504, Mauritius

Printed at: see last page
ISBN: 978-613-9-94142-1

*Acknowledgement*

*"Life without thankfulness is devoid of love and passion. Hope without thankfulness is lacking in fine perception. Faith without thankfulness lacks strength and fortitude. Every virtue divorced from thankfulness is maimed and limps along the spiritual road."*

**-John Henry**

At this amenity of successful integration of my work, I prostrate on the feet of **Lord Almighty**, who inculcated in me enough strength to complete my duties successfully.

It has been particularly rewarding and honorific to have the privilege of working under the able supervision of my respected major advisor, **Dr. Latika Sharma**, *Astt. Prof.*, Department of Agricultural Economics and Management, Rajasthan College of Agriculture, Udaipur, whose inspiring teaching, valuable guidance, timely remarks, untiring ceaseless efforts and erudite suggestions throughout the preparation of this dissertation and at every step are beyond capacity of my words to reciprocate with thankfulness. Her knowledge, wisdom and dedication towards this noble profession have always acted like a flame illuminating in my path.

I am extremely happy to express my deepest sense of gratitude to my respected teacher and co-guide, **Dr. S. S. Burark,** *Emeritus Scientist,* Department of Agricultural Economics and Management, Rajasthan College of Agriculture, Udaipur, whose constant encouragement and helpful suggestions helped me throughout the study period. His experiences as an economist and teacher have made him a constant oasis of ideas and passion in wisdom, which is exceptionally inspiring.

I am extremely thankful to **Dr. D. C. Pant** for his valuable suggestions and advice during my research work.

I extend my coordial thanks to **Dr. G. L. Meena, Sh. Hari Singh, Dr. B.R. Ranwah and Dr. H. K. Jain** for their co-operation and valuable suggestions given at the time of pre thesis presentation. I also express my sincere thanks to all the staff members of the Department of Agricultural Economics and Management, particularly **Sh. M. L. Gehlot, Ms. Annie Jacob, Sh. Dhakad and Mrs. Neetu.**

1

I would take this opportunity to thank, **Dr S. K. Chouhan**, Prof. Department of Agricultural Economics CSKHPKV, Palampur (H.P.) for providing guidance and support for the completion of my research work.

I place my thanks to my friends **Shalini, Soumya, Dimple, Divya, Pushpa and Sonia** for their moral support and encouragement for completion of manuscript. There are many anonymous well wisher and family members who directly and indirectly rendered me valuable help to complete this endeavour.

I bow my head at the feet of my loving parents, **Sh. H. L. Indoria & Smt. Sneh Indoria**, for suffering great agony to bring me up to this position. The most significant milestone of the life remains incomplete unless shared with those without whom life itself seems incomplete. Hence, in this opportune moment, I extend my profound gratitude towards the driving forces behind me, my husband **Mr. Manvendra Singh,** my lovely sister **Dr. Shama,** my brother in law **Dr. Anil Sharma** and my sweet nephews **Adityesh** and **Divyansh** without whom it was very difficult for me to achieve this goal in life as they always ease my burdens by their lovely smiles and support. I am extremely grateful for the affection and benediction of my family members, my elder brother **Mr. Ajay Indoria** and his wife **Mrs. Renu Indoria**.

*Place: Udaipur*                                                                          *(SHAILZA)*

# CONTENTS

## LIST OF TABLES

4

## LIST OF FIGURES

India is one of the fastest growing economies of the world and is currently the focus of a great deal of international attention. It is the seventh largest country in the world in terms of its geographical size. Today it has a population of nearly 1.2 billion which makes it the second most populous nation in the world. With current population growth, by 2025, India may even have caught up with China according to the UN.

Agriculture is one of the strongholds of the Indian economy and it accounted for 13.9 per cent of the gross domestic product (GDP) in 2011-12. Agriculture draws its significance from the vital supply and demand links with other sectors of the economy and is a major source of livelihood for the rural population of India. More than 58 per cent of the country's population depends on agriculture for its livelihood. India is the largest producer of coconut, mango, banana, milk and milk products, cashew nut, pulses, ginger, turmeric and black pepper in the world. It is also the second largest producer of rice, wheat, sugar, cotton, fruits and vegetables. Agricultural production is likely to increase significantly.

India has a large and diverse agriculture and is one of the world's leading producers, but its presence on the world market has been modest in relation to the size of its agriculture. Since independence, India has made a lot of progress in agriculture in terms of growth in output, yields and area under crops. It has gone through a Green Revolution (food grains), a White Revolution (milk), a Yellow Revolution (oilseeds) and a Blue Revolution (aquaculture). In recent years, there have been many changes in its agriculture and trade policies and significant changes in its net trade position for many individual products. The leading forecasting institutions expect that India will play a bigger role in world markets in future. In a number of markets it is expected to consolidate its position among the world's leading exporters (rice).

Now the question arises as to what are the main determinants of a supply function and demand function in export? The potential answer to this question has important policy implications. Standard models of export supply include explanatory variables such as export prices (relative contribution of improved export profitability), variable home and foreign costs, and productive capacity.

India's total agricultural product exports have a potentially large impact on world markets. The total exports from India in 2010-11 were Rs.900471.00 crore and total agricultural products exports were Rs.120185.95 crore which contributed 10.47 per cent to total export from India during 2010-11(Ministry of Agriculture). It indicated that India is a leading exporter of agricultural products. The Government's special efforts to encourage export of food grains in recent years through grant of World Trade Organization or WTO compatible subsidies has lead to India becoming one of the leading exporters of food grains in the international market. During 1990-91, Agricultural exports contributed 18.49% to the total exports i.e. Rs.6012.76 crores in value terms out of total exports which was Rs.32527.28 crores whereas in the year 2000-01, agricultural exports was Rs.28657.37crores as compared to total agricultural exports which was Rs.201356.45 crores (i.e. agricultural exports contributed 14.2% to the total exports during this fiscal year). This shows that over the years although agricultural exports are rising but their share in total exports is declining. This may be because the share of export of services has increased considerably over the time. There is also change in the composition of exports, agricultural products, such as jute and cotton, which were being exported in raw form in the 1950s, are now exported more as cotton yarn, fabrics, ready-made garments, coir yarn, and jute manufactures since the 1960s. The composition of agricultural and allied products for export changed primarily due to availability of better return through value addition and processing of agricultural products. This demand cut into the excess available for export in spite of a continuing desire, on the part of government, to shore up the invariant foreign-exchange shortage. In Fiscal Year 1960, tea was the major export by value. Oil cakes, cashew kernels, tobacco, raw cotton and spices were about equal in value but were only one-eighth of the value of tea exports. By Fiscal Year 1980, tea was still a major export commodity, however rice, coffee, fish, and fish products came close, followed by oil cakes, cashew kernels, and cotton.

Agriculture exports have assumed greater significance today than before because of the open market policies adopted by the government after WTO agreement. Indian agriculture now is more connected to world agriculture and any disturbances in production, prices or trade in agriculture commodities at one point instantly have an impact throughout the world market. India has only less than one per cent share of world market in agricultural exports. External environment problems do affect our exports but internal pricing strategies as well as non price factors also erode our competitiveness. Export earnings are dependent not only on domestic production and distribution situation but also on many external factors like export prices, countries competing in product trade, international consumer's product preferences and many other socio political factors. Due to high volatility of international prices, analysis of domestic and international prices is required to be undertaken from time to time. Further, most of our studies analyse agricultural exports at an aggregate level. So, it is difficult to draw easy interpretation and straight policy implications. Therefore, it is worthwhile to study export behaviour of an individual agricultural commodities and the factors influencing their demand and supply.

**Selection of Commodities**

In India like other developing countries, agriculture continues to be an important source of foreign exchange and revenue. For tapping the full potential of agricultural exports, it is essential that research and development should be done in such a way that it can have greater bearing on the production of a particular agricultural produce for the purpose of export on the one hand, and financial and fiscal incentives must be provided for exporting a particular produce after addressing all pre-harvesting and post-harvesting concerns on the other. India's trade policy on agricultural items is guided by twin objectives for ensuring food security and building export market for enhancing income of farmers, depending on domestic availability.

Tea, coffee and basmati rice are undoubtedly the most important and popular exporting commodity of India. Tea shows a high percentage share in production and exports of India. Also its export share relative to production was very high during early 1990's. From available data, it is evident that India is largest producer and consumer of tea in the world. Over the years, it has continued to be an important foreign exchange earner of the country. This is the only industry where India has retained it's leadership over last 15 years. During 1970-71, tea contributed 30.44% to the total agricultural exports in which the exported quantity was 199.1 thousand tones and its value was Rs.148.25 crores (Economic Survey 1983-84). Then during 1990-91, its contribution to the total agricultural exports fell down to 17.87% in which the exported quantity was 202 thousand tones and its value became Rs.1074.82 crores (Agricultural Statistics at Glance 2002). This shows that although the exported quantity and value had increased but its contribution to the total agricultural exports had fallen down. Later on during 2010-11, share of tea export to the total agricultural export was 0.3% with the exported quantity of 99.0 thousand tones valuing at Rs.1419 crore. (Economic Survey 2010-11). Thus, it is important to know the factors effecting the demand and supply situations of tea exports which are hindering the export of this important export commodity from India.

With the Indian economy poised to grow by 3% in the next few years, there is an opportunity for the coffee industry to increase footprints in the export market (Deputy Chairman Planning Commission). Coffee is also one of the most important exporting commodities of India as India ranks sixth among coffee producing countries in the world after Brazil, Vietnam, Colombia, Indonesia and Ethiopia with 2% share in global area under coffee. During 1970-71, coffee contributed 5.15% to the total agricultural exports having 32.20 thousand tones as quantity and Rs.25.11 crore as value (Economic Survey 1983-84). Later on during 1990-91, it declined a little bit to 4.21% of the total agricultural exports (i.e. 85.98 thousand tones in quantity and Rs.253.32 crore in value). Data shows that although quantity and value has increased but share has declined as compared to total agricultural exports (Agricultural Statistics at a Glance 2002). During 2010-11, its share in total agricultural exports fell down to 0.37% with exported quantity of 115.0 thousand tones and Rs.1275 crores in value (Economic Survey 2010-11).

Basmati rice is also the major contributor in total foodgrain exports of India. Exports of basmati rice fluctuated between nearly 30-40 % during the last few decades. The second most important contributor was non basmati rice which accounted for nearly 18% of food grain exports. Thus, these two groups together accounted for approximately 90 % of the total food grain exports during 1990-93. During 1970-71, percentage share of rice in total agricultural exports was 1.03% having 32.8 thousand tones as quantity and Rs.5.03 crore as value (Economic Survey 1983-84). Later on during 1990-91, percentage share of basmati rice to the total agricultural exports became 7.31% having 527.47 thousand tones and Rs.439.95 crore quantity and value, respectively (Agricultural Statistics At a Glance 2002). During the triennium 1993 to 1996, basmati rice exports declined drastically from 72.16 % to 35.4 % of total food grain exports. For basmati rice of India, Saudi Arabia is the biggest market. For export promotion of any commodity, quality consideration is very important. It is very distressing to note that a developing country like Indonesia whose socio-economic conditions are similar to India has banned the imports of non-basmati rice from India (Rangi and Sidhu,1999) due to quality control measures. Similarly during the year 1996, the food ministry of Bangladesh decided to dump into sea over 3700 tones of rice imported from India (Anonymous,1996), as this rice was found to be unfit for human consumption (Rangi and Sidhu, 2001). These events lead to a negative impact on agricultural exports from India. During 2011-12, in India share of basmati rice in total exports was 9.3% and that of non basmati rice was 5.4%. Out of the total farm export of 82480 crores in 2011-12 the share of basmati rice was 18.7% and that of non basmati rice was 10.5%. A year before, the share of basmati rice was 27.2% while non basmati rice was banned. The ban was lifted on Oct. 2011 after a long period of restriction.

Thus it is very important to study each commodity individually as, it will depict problem faced in exporting that particular commodity to the other countries. Tea and coffee were our traditional export commodities and there was wide overtime variation among the export of these commodities. So, it needs the attention of the researcher to study them individually. While taking rice under consideration it is also one of the important commodity of export. India has a monopolistic position in basmati rice market and the quality of Indian basmati is superior in aroma and taste to all other competing exporters of basmati. Thus basmati rice has good prospects of consolidating its position in world market and it is very important to study the factors affecting the demand and supply of basmati rice exports from India.

## 1.2   OBJECTIVES OF THE STUDY

Keeping in view the above consideration research study entitled **"Estimation of Demand and Supply Functions for the Export of Selected Agricultural Commodities from India"** was planned with specific objectives as under:

(1)   To study the growth rate and instability of exports of tea, coffee and basmati rice from India.

(2)   To analyse the destination wise pattern of exports of tea, coffee and basmati rice.

(3)   To estimate export demand and supply functions for tea, coffee and basmati rice.


## 1.3   LIMITATIONS OF THE STUDY

Though all possible efforts were made to make the study objective and precise but due to the paucity of time at the disposal of investigator, certain limitations did remain in the study, such limitations are:

(1)   The study is based on secondary sources of data and hence the accuracy of results depends on the accuracy with which the data were generated.

(2)    The data of exports in quantity and value terms of some crops were not available on continuous basis.

## 1.4    PLAN OF WORK

The entire study has been presented in five chapters. Chapter first deals with importance and objectives of the study. A comprehensive review of relevant study is given in chapter second. Chapter third deals with materials and methods adopted and analytical framework of the problem. Chapter fourth is meant to present the results of both investigation and a brief discussion on them. Summary and conclusion of the study are presented in chapter fifth. Bibliography is given at the end of the thesis.

Review of literature enables the investigator to acquire knowledge about the previous work done in concerned area of research and provides a foundation to the theoretical framework in addition to getting an insight into the methods and procedures followed. Available literature directly related to the current research and commodities as well as similar studies related to the other crops or techniques were reviewed. These reviews have been provided under the following headings:

2.1    Changes in the structure of exports of agricultural commodities, growth rate and instability analysis.

2.2    Destination wise pattern of export of selected agricultural commodities.

2.3    Export demand and supply functions of selected agricultural commodities.

## 2.1    REVIEWS RELATED TO CHANGES IN THE STRUCTURE OF EXPORTS OF AGRICULTURAL COMMODITIES, GROWTH RATE AND INSTABILITY ANALYSIS

**Murthy and Subrahmanyam (1999)** conducted a study on exports of onion from India and examined the trend of exports in different forms of onion, the change in the export markets at different period of time; and estimated the growth and instability in exports of onion. The growth rates were estimated to examine the rate of change in exports of onion during different time period. Co-efficient of variation was used as an index of instability. The quantity of export of onion from India to UAE, Saudi Arabia, Bangladesh and Srilanka was increased at very high and significant compound growth rates of 68 per cent, 44 per cent, 85 per cent and 31 per cent per annum, respectively during 1970-71 to 1994-95, which indicated good potential for export of onion to these countries in future also. Malaysia, Singapore and UAE had exhibited a relatively high quantity of exports which reflected in low stability index. It was only UAE which had shown the higher growth with less instability indicating consistency of UAE in importing higher quantum of onion over the years.

**Kaur and Rangi (2000)** conducted a study on growth performance of oilseeds in India. The compound growth rates of area, production and productivity were estimated for the overall period under study i.e. (1970-71 to 1997-98) and two sub periods i.e. period I (1970-71 to 1983-84) and period II (1984-85 to 1997-98). It was observed that during period I the maximum growth rate in area was achieved by soybean followed by sunflower. Similar trend was observed for production and yield of these crops. Both soybean and sunflower emerged as highly profitable oilseed crops in the country. The growth rates of production at all India level were 1.64, 6.29 and 4.18 per cent during sub periods and overall study period, respectively.

**Nawadkar and Birari (2000)** studied the India's share in production and export of fruits and vegetables. The study was based on the time series as well as cross sectional data on different aspects such as production, productivity, exports and imports of fruits and vegetables of different countries derived from the secondary sources. The details of area, production and productivity of fruits and vegetables depicted that during the year 1995-96, the total area under fruits in India was 33.57 lakh hectares that produced 415.07 lakh mt. of fruits. As such the productivity of fruits worked out to be 12.36 mt/ha at national level. The state wise analysis indicated that the area under fruits crop was maximum in Andhra Pradesh.

**Dahiya et al. (2001)** studied the trend and growth rate of area, production and yield of fruit crops in Haryana. Trend analysis of major fruit crops in Haryana from the period 1991-98 with respect to area, production and yield was carried out. Five equations mainly linear, compound logarithmic, Cob Douglas and exponential had been tried to analyse the trends in area, production and yield of fruit crops. However, on the basis of $R^2$ (coefficient of determination) the liner equation was selected for the trend analysis. The analysis indicated that the area and production in guava and ber showed statistically increasing trend. The area, production and yield of major fruit crops registered a compound growth rate of 8.67, 3.33 and -4.92 per cent in mango, 12.01, 11.63 and -1.21 per cent for guava, 6.38, 4.34 and -1.92 per cent in citrus and so on. The annual growth rate for fruit crops under area and production in the state registered a positive growth rate. On the basis of these findings, it was inferred that cultivation of fruit had good potential and could be economically viable alternative to the existing crop cultivation in Haryana.

**Singh and Chandra (2001)** analyzed growth trends in area, yield and production in paddy, coarse cereals and oilseeds at all India level for the period of 1975-98. The analysis revealed that higher growth rate in production of paddy and coarse cereals had been due to increase in yield while in wheat, due to increase in area and yield. In case of cereals the growth in production had been low. In pulses negative growth rate in area under gram crop and negative growth of yield in pigeon pea was observed.

**Mathur and Kumar (2001)** conducted a study entitled economic inquiry into growth and instability of India's agricultural exports. The temporal changes, growth and instability in India's exports of agricultural commodities during the period 1962-94 were examined. Exports of fruits and vegetables, oilseeds, fish and fishery products, and feeds had grown remarkably during the early 1990s as compared to the previous decade. Exports of cereals and cereal preparations, and sugar and honey were observed to be most volatile in the last 2 decades. Both total merchandise and agricultural trade showed deficits since 1962-65 but agricultural trade earned a surplus of $1349 million in 1990-94, indicating the positive impact of new liberalized trade policies.

**Sundaravaradarajan and Kumar (2001)** studied instability in cashew production and trade in India. The nature of instability was analysed by taking data in cashew production, quantity exported and quantity imported during period 1971-72 to 1998-99. For addressing the nature of instability in the growth of cashew production, export and import the following growth model was fitted.

$$Y = \alpha + \beta t$$

Where, Y = production/export/import in the year 't'.

$\alpha$ = intercept

$\beta$ = regression coefficient

t = time period in years.

From the estimated trend, the upper and lower point was examined and two separate regressions were estimated.

$$Y_1 = \alpha_1 + \beta_1 t$$

$$Y_2 = \alpha_2 + \beta_2 t$$

It was revealed that the introduction of high yielding varieties and improved agricultural practices induced greater variability in cashew production in India. It was inferred that the instability in growth in quantity of kernels exported and production of raw cashew decreased. It was also concluded that there was a desirable instability in terms of quantity of kernels exported and production of raw cashew, while there was undesirable instability in the quantity of raw cashew imported.

**Purbia (2002)** studied the trend, growth and instability in production of major crops in Rajasthan. The secondary data for 1970 to 2000 was used. The technique like compound growth rate, linear trend equation and instability indices were used.

$$\textit{Instability index } (I_1) = \frac{SD}{AM}$$

SD = Standard deviation of area/production/productivity of crops for a specified period.

AM = Arithmetic mean of area/production/productivity of crops.

$$\textit{Instability index } (I_2) = \frac{SD^*}{AM^*} \times 100$$

$SD^*$ = standard deviation of detrained area/production/productivity of crops.

$AM^*$ = arithmetic mean of area/production/productivity of crops in a specified period.

$$\textit{Instability index } (I_3) = CV \sqrt{(1 - R^2)}$$

CV = coefficient of variation of area/production/productivity of the crop.

$R^2$ = Coefficient of determination of the trend equation for original time series data on area/production/productivity. It was revealed from the analysis that the growth rates of area of wheat, rapeseed and mustard, maize, groundnut, rice, dry chillies, coriander, guar were positive and maize was found to be highly stable crop in area while wheat emerged highly stable crop in both production and productivity. It was concluded that strategy for the crops must aim to enhance the production and productivity growth without causing much inter year instability. Acc. to him $I_3$ method of calculating the instability was more convenient one as it involved coffiecient of variation in it.

**Hyma *et al.* (2003)** conducted a study on export performance of onion and potato from India. In this study an attempt was made to ascertain the export performance of onion and potato in India, during the period 1970-71 to 1999-2000. The study was based on secondary data regarding quality, value and unit value of onion and potato exports from India which were obtained from DGCI & S, Kolkata. The domestic wholesale prices of onion and potato prevailed during 1996-97 to 1999-2000 were obtained from National Informatic Centre (NIC), Hyderabad. In the study various statistical tools like, growth rate, coefficient of variation and Coppocks's instability index were used. The export competitiveness of onion and potato was assessed by using nominal protection coefficient and Kendall's coefficient of concordance test was used to find out whether there is a significant agreement among all the exporters selected. During the overall period (1970-71 to 1999-2000) the quality of onion and potato exports from India registered a positive and significant growth rate of 6.27 per cent and 4.38 per cent per annum. Exports earning and unit value realization exhibited significant positive growth rate of 16.70 per cent, 12.28 per cent and 9.74 per cent and 7.45 per cent for onion and potato respectively during the same period.

**Sujata *et al.* (2003)** analysed the export scenario of mangoes from India. The study was based on the secondary data from 1989-90 to 2001-2002 collected from the APEDA. The total period was divided into two parts i.e. 1989-90 to 1994-95 (pre-WTO) and 1995-96 to 2001-2002 (post-WTO). The bifurcation of total period was done to know the effect of WTO on exports of mangoes. The basic statistics viz. Arithmetic mean (X), standard deviation (SD) and coefficient of variation (CV) were estimated for each period and overall period to know the average position and variability in the exports of mangoes. The study concluded that in spite of potentialities in production base, India's export of mangoes was not encouraging due to higher taxation, poor quality, lack of infrastructure, export promotion activities and research and development.

17

**Misra and Rao (2003)** examined trade policy, agricultural growth and rural poor: Indian experience, 1978-79 to 1999-2000. This study analysed whether trade liberalization helped to accelerate agricultural growth and reduced poverty in India. Specifically, it examined (i) how changes in trade policy introduced during the 1990s in India had influenced the domestic intersectoral terms of trade; (ii) the impact of terms of trade and trade policy among others on aggregate crop output and private investment in agriculture; (iii) whether trade policy and devaluation of the rupee among others had helped in raising agricultural exports; and (iv) how aggregate crop output and terms of trade had influenced rural poverty and real agricultural wages of unskilled workers. It was revealed in the study that new trade policy lead to a significant result on intersectoral terms of trade due to which private investment had increased producing a direct impact on increase in aggregate crop output. Misra and Rao also concluded that as a result of this whole change rural population got employment to such an extent that rural poverty had been eliminated. Above all the country's economic growth had improved to a considerable extent.

**Velavan (2004)** conducted a study entitled "Performance of cashew: a growth rate analysis". Time series data (for the years 1980-2000) on cashew area, production, exports and imports in India were analysed. It was revealed that cashew nut production had increased from 1.8 lakh tonnes in 1980-81 to 5.2 lakh tonnes in 1999-2000. The annual growth rate of cashew nut production was 4.94%. The production growth rate was lower in the post-liberalization period (1991/92-1999/2000) than that in the pre-liberalization period (1980/81-1990/91). However, the area growth rate increased in the post-liberalization period. Cashew exports from India increased from 26 257 MT in 1980-81 to 47 MT in 1998-99. The export growth rate was 6.31% and the import growth rate was 20.89% per year. This shows that India was highly dependent on imports to meet its domestic demand. Constraints in the production, export and marketing of cashew nut in India were outlined.

**Kaur et al. (2004)** conducted a study about the export of turmeric; its status and prospects, based on secondary data obtained from various issues of Indian agricultural publications and Agricultural Statistics at a Glance. Simple statistical tools like growth rate and percentage were used for analysis. The compound growth rate of area and production of turmeric was worked out by fitting the exponential function ($y = ab^t$). Least square method was used for making projections for the production and exports of turmeric for the year 2010

AD and 2020 AD. The best fit line showed an increasing trend that in 2010, production would be 7,36,023 million tones and exports would be 59,036 million tones in the same year. In percentage terms, in 2000-01, 5.83 per cent of turmeric production was being exported by India which would increase to 6.6 per cent in 2010 and further to 6.8 per cent in 2020 AD.

**Sadavati (2006)** conducted a study on export of basmati rice. In the study, an attempt was made to study the export scenario of basmati rice with specific objectives of analyzing the direction and changing pattern of exports. The analysis was done with the help of time series data covering the period from 1980-81 to 2000-01 at all India level, by employing Markov Chain model that captured the net effect in change in the exports. Results of the study revealed that there were five major countries importing Indian basmati rice namely, Saudi Arabia, Kuwait, UK, USA and UAE, which accounted for 80-90 per cent in 2000-01. The result of Markov Chain analysis revealed that the exports would likely to be concentrated in Saudi Arabia and Kuwait in future. A high dependence on one or two export markets would increase the trade risk in the long run. Therefore, appropriate export promotion strategies had to be evolved to diversify the geographical concentration.

**Mohanakumar (2008)** conducted a study on sources of instability in natural rubber price: an analysis in the post-reform phase. The study analysed the stability/instability and the sources of instability in natural rubber price during pre and post-liberalisation periods. In the pre-liberalisation period, supply side variable contributed to the volatility in natural rubber price. It appeared to be rather logical because the rate of growth in demand for natural rubber derived from the rate of growth in gross domestic product, which had grown more or less at a constant rate until 1991-92. On the contrary, demand for natural rubber became more volatile in the post-liberalisation period as part of it originated from the export market in the form of demand for rubber based manufactured products. As a result, demand side variable too contributed significantly to natural rubber price instability in the post-liberalisation period. The contribution to natural rubber price instability from supply side factor still remained robust resulting to a cumulative effect on price instability in the domestic market during the post-liberalisation phase. The macroeconomic implication of the finding was that the natural rubber price formation was increasingly being shifted from domestic market to international market and, therefore, any change in the world economic scenario might leave profound impact on NR price in the domestic market in the post-liberalisation phase.

**Pal (2010)** had studied growth and instability in production and export of Indian lac. The study to examine the growth and instability in production and export of Indian lac was based on secondary data collected for 38 years spanning from 1970-71 to 2007-08. The data were analyzed by using exponential function and instability index. The study revealed that during the overall period, production of Indian lac registered a declining trend while, the period from 2000-01 to 2007-08 was comparatively far better with positive growth rate and lower instability than the past three decades of lac production in India. The export quantity also registered a declining trend during overall period while, total export value and unit value of export registered positive and significant trend. Instability was more in total export value and unit value of export in comparison to export quantity.

**Chaudhari and Pawar (2010)** examined growth, instability and price analysis of pigeonpea (Cajanus cajan L.) in Marathwada region. During this study an attempt had been made to estimate growth and magnitude of variability in area, production and productivity of pigeonpea, seasonal variation, relationship between market arrivals and prices of pigeonpea in Marathwada region of Maharashtra State. Time series data for the period 1985-86 to 2004-05 regarding area, production and productivity were collected from Epitoma of Agriculture, published by Government of Maharashtra. The data regarding arrivals and prices were collected from four APMCs viz., Latur, Udgir, Osmanabad and Paranda for the same period. Compound growth rate, coefficient of variation, ratio to moving average method and double log model were used for achieving the objectives. The result revealed that among the districts, Jalna and Nanded showed significant positive growth in area and production of pigeonpea, while all districts and region recorded higher variability in area, production and productivity of pigeonpea. The maximum arrivals of pigeonpea was recorded in the month of January in all the selected markets, while significant negative relationship between arrivals and prices of pigeonpea was observed in Latur market.

**Bera et al. (2011)** studied growth and instability of food grains production of India and West Bengal. The study attempted to examine the growth and instability in food grains production both at the country as well as state level (West Bengal) for the period ranging from 1950 to 2006 and also to found out the impact of modern crop production practices designated as green revolution technology occurred during mid-sixties on the same. The study revealed that India attained an overall growth rate in area, production and productivity of 284.22, 3028.02 and 22.29 percent, respectively and their corresponding instability measured in terms of adjusted co-efficient of variation were accounted to be 2.91, 0.36 and 0.05 percent, respectively. West Bengal witnessed acceleration at the rate of 29.29, 224.08 and 29.37 percent associated with the variability of 3.14, 01.47 and 1.90 percent respectively at the same order. In spite of experiencing a marginal set back in area under total food grains during post revolution period, production growth rate had become almost double in India due to almost two times higher productivity rise compared to pre-revolution period. In West Bengal, food grains production rose by 275.64 percent as a result of combined effect of rise in area and productivity by 13.95 and 39.28 percent respectively which were far ahead of that achieved prior to adoption of new technology. Both the country and state gained more stability in production and productivity front but the fluctuation of above parameters were recorded to be higher at country level in comparison to the state although the state experienced a higher rate of growth. Status of pulses and cereals, major component of total food grains, remained more or less static in India and in case of West Bengal, area and production registered a negative growth rate in spite of remarkable improvement in productivity, i.e. technological revolution in agricultural sector bypassed pulses, although the crops achieved more stability in productivity and production compared with regime of traditional crop production system.

**Thomas and Sheikh (2012)** studied growth and composition of Indian agricultural exports during reform era and analysed the emerging world demand for Indian agricultural commodities. Indian agricultural exports had increased manifolds. However, the contribution of agricultural export in the total export of the country had declined. Present study explored the growth performance of India's agricultural exports from 1991-92 to 2009-10, using compound annual growth rate and percentage share in total export of India as well as Gross Domestic Product. An in depth composition and structure analysis of the agricultural export was undertaken. The study also examined the changing dynamics of the contribution of individual group of commodities in the basket of agricultural export.

## 2.2 DESTINATION WISE PATTERN OF EXPORT OF SELECTED AGRICULTURAL COMMODITIES.

**Rangi *et al.* (2001)** conducted a study on export of basmati rice from India. Following an overview of global trade in rice (basmati and non-basmati) during 1996-99, this study examined the quantity of exports of basmati rice from India as well as the destination of exports during 1987/88-1997/98. Export prices of rice (basmati and non-basmati) from India during 1987/88-1996/97 were also examined, as well as the price spread of basmati rice through the main export channel (i.e. the Punjab Markfed Marketing Cooperative) for the year 1998-99. Then suggestions were presented to achieve a sustained export market for Indian basmati rice. It was concluded that export of commodity under study achieved a significant growth during the study period. Basmati rice contributed a major share in the export of agricultural commodity from India and further increase in its export would certainly help in improving the country's position in the export market.

**Raikhy (2003)** studied India's agricultural exports in the post-liberalisation period: problems and prospects.The commodity-wise and country-wise export performance of agricultural and allied products for the period 1992/93-1998/99 was analysed. It was concluded that internal and external trade policy reforms have resulted to higher increases in exports of agricultural and allied products, their diversification, and the wider spread of export destinations. However, the bulk of India's agricultural exports still conformed to traditional items.

**Sharma and Sharma (2003)** studied production and export performance of Indian tea - a temporal and cross-sectional analysis. Using historical data up to the year 1999, this paper examined: (i) the changes in the share of different districts/states in the total area and production of tea in India, as well as the growth rate in area, production and yield of tea both at the all-India and district/state levels; (ii) the contribution of area and yield and their combined effect on the growth of tea production in different districts/regions; and (iii) the growth of Indian tea exports over time and the changes in the share of different destination countries in total tea exports in the post-liberalization and WTO regime. It was revealed that share of different districts and states had increased especially in the northern and eastern hilly regions where there exists the problem of acidic soils and soil erosion and the growth rate of tea production was much higher in the post-independence period compared to that in the pre-independence period. As a result of which Indian tea got special place in world export market and various countries prefer Indian tea because of its quality.

**Silva and Da Carvalho (2004)** studied destination of Brazilian agricultural exports. This study described the evolution of Brazilian agricultural exports and their destinations during 1990 and 2002 by product groups. It showed that although Brazilian agriculture maintained its export market share, the sector experienced a decline in relative importance in world trade. Exports of raw agricultural products showed larger growth rates than those of manufactured products. Regarding destination, Brazilian agricultural exports converged to emerging countries and continued to show a concentration on a few products.

**Tejaswi *et al.* (2006)** studied direction of trade and changing pattern of Indian coffee exports - an application of Markov chain analysis. Among the plantation crops, coffee contributed significantly to India's economy, in addition to earning substantial foreign exchange for the country. Indian coffee production was approximately 3 lakh tonnes and exports were 213472 tonnes in 2001-02. Using the estimated transitional probabilities, the export of coffee to various destinations was predicted by multiplying the same with the respective market shares of the base year. It was evident from the results that USA was the most reliable and loyal importing country (loyalty index with the probability of 80% retention than that of other importing countries), followed by countries like Russian Federation etc.

**Sedaghat *et al* (2008)** examined study of structural changes in trade directions of Pistachio from Iran. Aims of the study were to examine the trade directions of Pistachio from Iran to major importing countries. Destination-wise time series data on export of Pistachio from Iran was collected for the period 1996-2003. Markov chain analysis and transitional probability matrix was used for the purpose of the study. The results showed that Emirate was the most loyal importer of Iranian Pistachio with the retention probability of 67.79 per cent followed by Russia (40.77) and Germany (33.36). Japan with retention probability of 5.91 per cent, Hong-Kong (5.68%), Taiwan (0%) and Spain (0%) were the most unstable markets for Iranian Pistachio export.

**Matos *et al.* (2008)** analysed the direct exports of Brazilian cooperatives. This study examined the cooperatives' direct exports by examining the performance of the main products sold, the destination countries and the major states' representation in the light of the macroeconomic situation. According to the results in 2007, exports amounted to US$3.30 billion under the leadership of agricultural cooperatives, and the main products exported were derived from the sugarcane sector, the soybean complex and the meat segment.

**Singh and Shukla (2010)** studied export performance and potential of mango in mango export zone Lucknow (UP) .This analysis reported the results of a study conducted during 2007-08 on the status and prospects of mango export in the mango-export zone in Lucknow, Uttar Pradesh, India. Secondary data was obtained from various published and unpublished sources such as office of the DHO Lucknow, Mango Pack House Lucknow, published report of NHB, District Statistical Patrika, Annual Reports of CISH, Journals and Books. Tabulated data were provided on (i) year-wise mango export and revenue, (ii) year-wise projection of mango export, and (iii) country- and cultivar-wise mango export, from the mango export zone in Lucknow. The study revealed that Saudi Arabia, Kuwait and United Kingdom were the important markets for Indian mangoes. Maximum export took place from the lucknow region of U.P. as the climatic conditions were favourable for the cultivation of mango which showed high potentials of further expansion of export market of mango from India.

**Deshmukh (2010)** studied export competitiveness of horticultural sector in India; commodity wise analysis. This study examined India's share in world trade of horticultural products, the performance of horticultural sector trade in terms of changes in exports of various horticultural products, growth trends and variability in exports of various horticultural products and the export competitiveness of India's horticultural products. The study was based on time series data for the years. The results revealed that India's exports of fruits in quantity terms increased from 102 thousand tonnes in 1991 to 488 thousand tonnes in 2010 and in value terms this increase is Rs. 348 crore in 1991 and Rs. 3,404 crore in 2010. The export quantity increased by more than four times in the last 15 years and the value of exports by 10 times. The major fruits exported in terms of quantity are mango (53.5 thousand tonnes), grapes (38.9 thousand tonnes), orange (31.5 thousand tonnes), apple (23.2 thousand tonnes), banana (12.8 thousand tonnes), other citrus fruits (11.4 thousand tonnes) and lemon (10.5 thousand tonnes). In value terms grapes and mango exports earn the maximum foreign exchange for India. In this way Indian horticulture sector got a special momentum in terms of export competitiveness among other countries.

**Angles et al. (2011)** studied impact of globalization on production and export of turmeric in India - an economic analysis. India was a major supplier of turmeric to the world with more than 60 per cent share in turmeric trade. The production and export performance of turmeric in India had been examined using secondary data for the period from 1974-75 to 2007-08 and exponential form of growth function was used for the analysis. The growth in production and export of turmeric was reported significant, because of the high demand coupled with inflation. Instability index was worked for the production and export for preliberalization and post-liberalization periods. Instability had been observed high for production, export and prices of domestic and international markets. For the assessment of direction of trade, the Markov chain model was used. The data regarding country-wise export of turmeric showed that the previous export share retention for Indian turmeric had been high in minor importing countries (pooled under others category) (87%), followed by UAE (49%), Iran (41%) and UK (35%). The countries such as USA and Japan were not the stable importers of Indian turmeric. The plans for export might be oriented towards these two countries and also plans should be formulated for stabilizing the export of turmeric to other countries. They suggested that farmers should be provided training on production of a quality product.

## 2.3  ESTIMATION OF DEMAND AND SUPPLY FUNCTIONS.

**Raju (1990)** studied a economic analysis of cultivation and export of coriander. Coriander (Coriandrum sativum) is an important spice in India, widely used as a flavouring agent in cooking and the preparation of tobacco-products. Its production, however, experienced considerable fluctuation over the last 20 years. This study examined patterns of cultivation of coriander in the country and identified the factors that affect output levels. It also evaluated the prospects for exporting the product. An estimated equation revealed that both lagged yield and lagged price emerged as significant variables in determining cultivators planting decisions. State-wise analysis showed that Andhra Pradesh was the largest producer of coriander in 1982/83 followed by Rajasthan, Madhya Pradesh, Tamil Nadu and some other states. In 1986/87, however Rajasthan became the largest cultivator and had continued to be as such. In terms of exports, the largest exporter of coriander was Morocco. Although the export quantity from India had been increasing it was negligible compared to the demand levels in major consuming countries like USA, Saudi Arabia and Germany. Hence, it was recommended that India raise its exports of coriander to these countries as well as raise productivity levels to compete in the international market for the product.

**Singh and Singh (1991)** studied India's agricultural exports - problems and prospects. In spite of heavy industrialization in India, agriculture continued to be the dominant sector of the economy. This study assessed the performance of agriculture as a foreign exchange earner for the country, in light of its mounting deficit in the balance of payments. A detailed analysis was pursued with respect to India's export share in the world market, changing trends in agricultural exports and the general direction of trade for products such as tobacco, nuts, tea and oilseeds. It was concluded that agricultural performance in terms of exports had been poor due to several internal and external constraints. The domestic infrastructure was inefficient leading to uneconomic costs and demand pressure from the local population. Quality and other non-price factors added to these bottlenecks. Internationally, the protectionist barriers being built up and maintained by developed countries made it difficult for India and other developing countries to earn enough foreign exchange. Thus it was suggested that there was a need to initiate changes on both fronts if agriculture was to make its maximum potential contribution to trade in India.

**Athukorala (1991)** conducted a study on an analysis of demand and supply factors in agricultural exports from developing Asian countries. This study examined the relative importance of external demand conditions and internal supply factors for agricultural export performance, drawing upon the experience of India, Indonesia, Malaysia, Pakistan, the Philippines, Sri Lanka and Thailand over the period 1960-86. The results ran counter to the conventional view that growth of agricultural exports from developing countries depended predominantly on the world market factors over which they had no control. While external demand certainly played an important role, a country could expand its exports under given world market conditions by improving upon its market share in its traditional exports and diversifying into new export lines, provided it pursue appropriate domestic economic policies. As regards prospects for export diversification, an analysis of the comparative export performance of sample countries demonstrated that countries which maintained open-type economies with flexible adjustments to changing world market conditions were able to switch from one line of agricultural exports to another. The results supported the view that relative export success of individual countries emanated mostly from active supply-side policies as against passive acceptance of external demand conditions.

**Sandhu (1993)** studied India's export share of black pepper in the world trade - an econometric analysis. The study examined export demand, income and export market share elasticities in important market segments for Indian exports using a double logarithmic function. An attempt was made to deal with exchange rate fluctuations, domestic inflationary trends, currency devaluations and other transitory trend effects. Structural and directional transformations were also incorporated. Derived demand estimates for Indian black pepper were estimated for: (1) export demand and income elasticities in general (1950/51-1987/88); (2) export demand and income elasticities in the USSR market (1955/56-1987/88); and (3) export market share elasticities of trade with the USA as compared with market share of Indonesia and Brazil. Supply problems had advesely afffected trade. It was revealed that Indian pepper had been facing stiff competition in the US market, but circumstances are favourable for its expansion due to rising per capita demand because of its qualitative aspects.

**Veena et al. (1994)** studied factors affecting export demand elasticity for Indian coffee. Coffee was a major plantation crop cultivated in the states of Karnataka, Kerala and Tamil Nadu in India. This study noted the changes of the breakdown of the communist countries, previously large importers of Indian coffee; under these changed circumstances it was tried to identify the factors which were responsible for increasing Indian coffee exports. It estimated separately the demand from developed countries, and from the former communist states. Data from a 25 year period, 1966-90 was used. The developed countries considered for the purpose of export demand elasticity analysis were the USA, GFR, Italy, and the Netherlands, while the USSR and Yugoslavia were the two communist countries considered. Exports to the developed countries were affected by the world price for coffee, and other major exporters, for example Brazil, were highly competitive. However Indian coffee exports to communist countries were dependent on bilateral agreements rather than market forces. The study concluded that the price realisation for Indian coffee exports in the world market was low, and that India should try to increase exports to the developed countries, particularly considering the disruption of the former communist countries.

**Indira (1995)** studied coffee marketing under regulatory regime. The analysis was conducted of the working towards the pooled system under the control of the Indian Coffee Board. The study discussed coffee production in India, the genesis of a regulatory system, functions assigned to the Coffee

Board, the international situation, export auction and ICO indicator prices, the relationship between export auction and domestic prices, grower's returns and cost of coffee cultivation. Market intervention in the form of a statutory board had helped in maintaining price stability in the internal market. Despite the promotional efforts of the Board, internal consumption had been stagnant. Under the intervention policy, consumers were over-protected at the expense of producers. The study revealed that coffee marketing under regulatory regime served a major function in the growth and promotion of coffee export market. Earlier coffee marketing without any regulatory measure will lead to the unwanted losses. This made Indian coffee to sustain a reputed position in the world coffee market which further increased its demand. Various other measures were also identified to regulate the coffee export in an efficient manner so that supply of Indian coffee could made available so as to compensate the increasing demand in the world market.

**Agrawal (1990)** studied Oilseeds in India - perspectives for 2001 A.D. Statistical/econometric methods were used to estimate demand for edible oils and supply of oilseeds up to the year 2001. The per capita consumption expenditure on edible oils had increased at a faster rate than the per capita consumption expenditure on food as a whole. The elasticities of edible oils consumption were higher for the poor than for the non-poor. An analysis of growth rates of oilseeds and other agricultural products indicated that growth rates of rice and wheat were 2.8% and 5.4% per annum, respectively, while that of oilseeds was only 2.5% per annum over the period 1968/69-1983/84. The supply projection of oilseed suggested that if the gains of the Sixth Five Year Plan were maintained in the future, India might not only be able to save on foreign exchange, but might be able to export surplus oilseeds. The main constraints in accelerating oilseeds production were (1) preponderance of rainfed farming; (2) non-utilization of modern inputs and improved agricultural implements; (3) inadequate availability of certified seeds; (4) susceptibility of oilseed crops to pests and diseases; and (5) inadequate price support.

**Bordoloi et al. (2003)** studied variations in production, export and domestic consumption of tea: an econometric study. Trends in tea production, exports and domestic consumption in India, Sri Lanka and Kenya during the period 1971-2000 were analysed using dummy variables and linear regression models. It was revealed that India had maintained consistent, sustained growth (2.20% per annum) in production in spite of decreasing exports (-0.48% per annum). Its dwindling export market was largely compensated by increasing domestic consumption (3.41% per annum). Kenya had also maintained consistent and sustained growth in production (5.56% per annum) and exports (5.70% per annum). Its domestic consumption had shown an annual growth rate of 4.5%. Sri Lankan tea, on the other hand, had maintained a moderate growth rate in production (1.17% per annum) and exports (1.10% per annum). Among the three countries, Kenya had achieved the highest annual growth rate in production, exports and domestic consumption during 1971-2000. Quantity-wise, India's increase in yield and domestic consumption per annum were the highest while Kenya remained the top exporter.

**Dellal and  Koc (2003)** conducted a study entitled an econometric analysis of apricot supply and export demand in Turkey. They estimated a supply model for apricots and an export demand model for dried apricots for Turkey, using data obtained in 2000 and 2001, to provide unit-free measure coefficients for better supply and marketing management. Using parameter estimates from the models and sample average data, elasticities of long-run supply, price-yield and export of dried apricots were computed as 0.72, 0.54 and -0.87, respectively. From the price dependent export demand model, the price flexibility of dried apricots was calculated as -0.71. The import demand elasticities of dried apricots for major destination countries were estimated and found to be inelastic. An evaluation of aggregated household consumption expenditure data indicated that the demand for fresh apricots would increase as per capita real income, population and urban population go up. However, the growth in domestic demand for dried apricots and apricot jam would gradually increase as per capita income, population and urban population go up. According to the supply and export demand elasticities of dried apricots, without either supply control or demand expansion, apricot growers' income would not be stabilized.

**Niemi (2003)** studied cointegration and error correction modelling of agricultural commodity trade: the case of ASEAN agricultural exports to the EU.

The objective of this study was to build a set of dynamic, theory-based econometric models which were able to capture both short-run and long-run effects of income and price changes, and which could be used for prediction and policy simulation under alternative assumed conditions. Econometric models were constructed for 7 agricultural commodities (cassava, cocoa, coconut oil, palm oil, pepper, rubber, and tea) exported from the Association of

Southeast Asian Nations (ASEAN) to the European Union (EU) from 1961-2000. The import demand analysis of the study examined two key features: the response of EU's agricultural commodity imports to income and price changes; and the length of time required for this response to occur. The estimations of the export demand relationships provided tests whether the exporters' market shares were influenced by the level of relative export price, and whether exports were affected by variations in the rate of growth of imports. The export supply analysis examined the relative influence of real price and some non-price factors in stimulating the supply of exports. The lag distribution (the shape and length of the lag) was found to be very critical in export supply relationships, since the effects of price changes usually took a long time to work themselves through and since the transmission of the price effects could be complex. The set of dynamic econometric models estimated in the study were then used to simulate the effects of different types of trade policies. More specifically, attempts were made to quantify the effects of a unilateral tariff removal by the EU, an imposition of export subsidies and taxes by the ASEAN countries as well as exchange rate adjustments on ASEAN agricultural exports to the EU. The results suggested that concepts such as co integration and error correction specification were well suited for the study of agricultural trade flows, which were typically non-stationary time series. Furthermore, the study showed the importance of inspection of the time series properties and the examination of both short- and long-run adjustment when studying trade functions. The different dynamic responses were often critical to the outcomes of the types of trade policies considered.

**Chern and Yu (2003)** analysed China's agricultural export and import behavior. They estimated the export supply and import demand for agricultural commodities in China, using annual and quarterly time-series data for the period 1980-92. The regression results showed that the exports of grains (rice and soybeans) were determined mostly by domestic output rather than relative prices. On the other hand, the relative prices (export price over domestic price) were the key factors affecting the export of pigmeat and aquatic products in China. The results revealed further that the exports of vegetables were affected by acreage, not prices. The results also indicated that increasing the income in the future would reduce the exports of pigmeat, aquatic products and fruits. The estimated models of import demand showed that the imports of grains (mostly wheat) were determined by relative prices, domestic output, and per capita household income. Increasing income would be the key factor for increasing wheat import in the future. On the other hand, the import demand for sugar was affected mostly by output and moderately by income and relative prices.

**Chadha (2007)** conducted a study entitled "Changing structure of demand for agricultural commodities: preparing for the future". The study dealt with changes into the demand-side, both in the domestic and external markets. For domestic demand analysis, focus was on items and product lines directed to human consumption alone; indirect demand for cereals and other eating stuff, for producing, say, meat, egg and poultry, was not examined. The study revealed that an increasing or a declining output share of a sub-sector in agriculture was, at best, only a rough reflection of the changing consumer preferences and choices. The implications of the demand-side analysis for supply adjustments and the concomitant policy initiatives needed for modifying, creating or strengthening market infrastructures especially for catering to the export market.

**Kumar and Muraleedharan (2007)** studied SPS regulations and competitiveness of Indian spice exports. This study investigated India's export performance of spices (whole pepper and capsicum) in the markets of the Organization for Economic Cooperation and Development (OECD) and South and Southeast Asia, which constituted a substantial market for Indian spices. A Constant Market share model was used to decompose the growth in exports of spices into size of the market effect, market composition effect and competitiveness effect. The analysis was performed for the exports during the nineties, the period India had to resort to increased challenges of food safety. The study confirmed that there was not substantial trade effect for Indian spices due to quality issues, such as sanitary and phytosanitary regulations. This study argued that increase in exports to neighbouring regions was explained more by the increased demand and supply and not by the stringent quality requirements of traditional importing countries.

**Devarajaiah *et al.* (2010)** estimated trends in export of rice from India. Rice export constituted a considerable share in the national exports in general, and in agricultural exports in particular. There was a good scope for India to take advantage of the new trade opportunities for sustaining the export of rice. Export of rice from India reached an all time high record and earned foreign exchange to the tune of Rs. 7035.88 crores during 2006-07. There was year to year fluctuations in both the quantity and value of basmati, as well as non-Basmati rice exports from India. Though variations were observed, there was a consistent growth in rice exports over the years. The reasons attributed to these fluctuations mainly included, production and productivity level of both basmati and non-basmati rice in India and other export competing countries, Government export policy in order to maintain price stability, and adequate domestic supplies etc.

**Mendhe and Degaonkar (2010)** studied export performance of Indian chilli. There was immense scope to expand India's export potential of chilli (*Capsicum annuum L.*) and detailed analyses of export trade of chilli was studied. They observed that high priority should be given to increase the production and productivity of chilli. This was necessary to meet the increasing domestic demand on one hand and to build up a sustained supply to meet international markets for earning foreign exchange through chilli export in other hand. Markov chain analysis revealed that there was huge scope to expand the export of chilli to Malaysia, Sri Lanka, Singapore, USA, UK and other countries. Therefore, appropriate export promotion strategies had to be evolved to diversify the geographical concentration for chilli export. Also steps should be initiated to capture the world markets on a sustained basis through international trade fair, exhibitions could be arranged to gain knowledge about quality preferences and thereby measures could be taken to export chilli in the needy market.

**Kumar et al. (2011)** estimated demand elasticity for food commodities in India. The food demand in India was examined in the context of a structural shift in the dietary pattern of its population. The food demand behaviour was explained using a set of demand elasticities corresponding to major food commodities. The demand elasticities were estimated using multi-stage budgeting with QUAIDS model and another alternative model, FCDS. The study revealed that the estimated income elasticities vary across income classes and were lowest for cereals group and highest for horticultural and livestock products. The analysis of price and income effects based on the estimated demand system had suggested that with increase in food price inflation, the demand for staple food (rice, wheat and sugar) might not be affected adversely but, that of high-value food commodities was likely to be affected negatively. Therefore, the study cautioned that if inflation in food prices remained unabated for an extended period, there was the possibility of reversal of the trend of diversification and that of consumers returning to cereal-dominated diet, thus accentuating under-nourishment.

**Roy (2011)** conducted a study entitled "Behavior of India's horticultural exports: does price competitiveness play a determining role". The impact of price factors on the exports of horticultural products from India during 1961 to 2005 was investigated. Some of the major destinations were Bangladesh, Malaysia, Nepal, UAE and UK. It was revealed that the impact of price factors surpassed that of non-price factors including production and world demand.

This chapter deals with the methodology part to understand the conceptual framework of the functioning of the phenomenon and to accomplish the stated objectives of the study. The present study is designed to understand and analyze the growth rate, instability, demand and supply functions of coffee, tea and basmati rice and the destination wise pattern of exports of these commodities. To make the picture more complete, principle topics such as study area, data base and analytical tools employed in the investigation are briefly given in this chapter.

## 3.1    STUDY AREA

India's share in the world trade in the agricultural commodities is low as it is a developing country. There is lot of competition due to the demand for high quality products and also the stringent legislation relating to health and safety standards of the importing country. India's agricultural exports include basmati rice, tea and coffee which contribute a major share in agricultural exports.

## 3.2    DATA BASES

The secondary data regarding quantity, value and unit value of exported agricultural products overtime were collected from various publications and websites of Ministry of Agriculture, Government of India, Director General of commercial Intelligence & Statistics, Ministry of Commerce, Kolkata., Ministry of Consumer Affairs, Food & Public Distribution, Govt. of India, Department of Commerce, Ministry of Commerce & Industry, Govt. of India and Central Statistical Organization (CSO), compiled by India Stat, Trade map, World development indicators, APEDA.

## 3.3    GROWTH RATE AND INSTABILITY ANALYSIS

## 3.3.1  GROWTH RATE ANALYSIS

The growth rate of agricultural exports and of unit prices was arrived by using the exponential growth function of the form

$$Y = ab^t U_t \qquad\qquad (3.1)$$

Where,

$$Y \quad = \quad \text{Export quantities of Tea/ Coffee/ Basmati Rice.}$$

$$a \quad = \quad \text{intercept}$$

$$b \quad = \quad \text{regression coefficient and}$$

$$t = \quad \text{time variable}$$

$U_t =$ error term

The equation was estimated after transforming (1) as follow

$$\log y = \log a + t \log b + \log U_t \tag{3.2}$$

Then, the per cent compound growth rate (g) was calculated using the relationship

$$g = \{\text{antilog of } (\log b)\text{-}1\} \times 100 \tag{3.3}$$

## 3.3.2 INSTABILITY ANALYSIS

In order to study the variability in the agricultural exports, an index of instability was used as a measure of variability. This was desirable from the point of view of measuring instability since it can be hypothesized that instability is a more serious phenomena when the level of foreign trade is low. First the deterministic component of the total variability in exports was calculated by fitting an exponential trend and taking arithmetic deviation of actual exports $y_t$ from predicted values $y_t$*. An index of instability was constructed which measures mean sum of squares of these deviations.

The instability was calculated by following methods:

i.) $\quad I_t = \sqrt{\dfrac{\sum U_t^2}{N}}$

Where,

$I_t$ = Index of instability

$U_t^2$ = deviation between actual ($y_t$) and trend values ($y_t$*), $U_t = y_t - y_t$*

N = no. of years

ii.) $\quad \text{C.V.} = \dfrac{SD^*}{AM^*} \times 100$

35

Where,

C.V. = coefficient of variation

$SD^*$ = standard deviation

$AM^*$ = arithmetic mean

## 3.4    PATTERN OF DESTINATION OF EXPORTS

As it has been stated earlier that India is the leading producer of various commodities and plays an important role in their exports. These commodities are exported to different countries depending on their demand and supply. So here arises the need to find that which commodity is being exported to which country. This was done by tabular analyses.

## 3.5    ESTIMATION OF DEMAND AND SUPPLY FUNCTION

Export demand and supply functions for three selected agricultural commodities namely tea, coffee and basmati rice was done separately with the help of econometric models using simultaneous equation method and elasticities for demand and supply of exports of these three commodities was calculated to support appropriate policy decisions.

In the trade literature, the assumption that a country having a small share in total world trade of a commodity faces perfectly elastic demand curve- the small country hypothesis – is quiet popular. But in the real world situation even a small country may find it difficult to sell all of its products at given prices in the world market. Transportation costs, supply lags, market imperfections and quantity considerations may be some of the possible reasons for this phenomenon. Therefore, it seems logical that even for a small country the export demand curve faced by it is downward slopping.

In the present study, export price is endogenously determined, subject to various shifters of supply and demand curves. Thus, the interrelationships between export demand and export supply need not to be restricted via the export price only and could be extended to include some other variables.

**Variables affecting Export Demand of a commodity:**

The following variables were hypothesized to be affecting Export Demand of a commodity:

i.  **Price of Export:** The amount of export quantity demanded of a commodity was supposed to be inversely related to the price of exports as per the law of demand applicable to normal goods.

ii. **World Export price level:** The world export price level variable was included to capture the effect of export prices of other principal exporting countries of the commodity competing in the world market. The variable was supposed to be positively related to the demand of exports of that commodity for the home country. The world export price level was calculated by taking weighted average of export prices of ten principal exporting countries of that commodity excluding India, the weights being the share of each exporting country in the total world exports of that commodity.

iii. **World Income Level:** The variable of world income level was included to capture the effect of real incomes of principal importing countries of the commodity from India. This variable was supposed to be positively related to the demand for exports of that commodity for the home country. The world income level was calculated by taking weighted average of real income of ten principal simporting countries of that commodity from India, the weight being the share of each importing country in the total exports of that commodity by the home country.

**Variables affecting Export Supply of a commodity:**

The following variables were hypothesized to be affecting export supply of a commodity:

i.  **Prices of Exports:** The amount of export quantity supplied of a commodity was supposed to be positively related to the prices of exports of that commodity as per the law of supply.

ii. **Supply Shock Variable:** This variable was included to depict the effect of fluctuation in the domestic production level of a commodity on its export supply. The positive supply fluctuations were hypothesized to be positively related to the export supply. It was measured as the deviation of year to year actual production from trend values of production and will be specified as a dummy variable with positive fluctuations carrying a value one and negative fluctuations carrying a value zero.

iii. **Demand Pressure Variable:** This variable was included in the model to depict the effect of fluctuations in the domestic demand pressure for a commodity on its export supply. The variable was supposed to be inversely related to the export supply. It was measured as deviation of year to year actual GNP from its trend value.

iv. **Time Trend:** Time trend variable was included in the model to account for combined effects of long term factors such as changes in technology, factor supply, infrastructure, and factor productivity which determine cost competitiveness of exports causing the supply curve to shift over time. The variable was expected to be positively related to the export supply over the time (there could, of course, be secular shifts which work negatively as well).

Bilateral and multilateral trade agreements also affect the export supply of the commodity. But these variables couldn't be included in the study because of quantitative and measurement problems.

**Econometric Model**

Separate models were specified for each of the selected commodities considering the following endogenous and exogenous variables:

**Endogenous Variables:** The value of the following variables was determined within the framework of an econometric model.

$Y_{1it}$ = Demand for Indian exports of $i^{th}$ commodity in $t^{th}$ year in thousand U.S. dollars.

$Y_{2it}$ = Supply of Indian exports of $i^{th}$ commodity in $t^{th}$ year in thousand U.S. dollars

$Y_{3it}$ = Export price of $i^{th}$ commodity in $t^{th}$ year in U.S.dollar per thousand metric tonnes.

**Predetermined Variables:**

a. **Exogenous variables:** The values of the following variables were not determined within the econometric model but they played a role in the determination of the values endogenous variables in the model.

$X_{1it}$ = World export price of $i^{th}$ commodity in $t^{th}$ year in U.S. dollar per thousand metric tonnes.

$X_{2it}$ = World real income in $t^{th}$ year at constant price.

$X_{3it}$ = Supply shock in the $i^{th}$ commodity during $t^{th}$ year in thousand metric tonnes specified as dummy (one for positive fluctuation, zero for negative fluctuations)

$X_{4t}$ = Demand pressure in $t^{th}$ year at constant price.

$X_{5i}$ = time trend of exports of $i^{th}$ commodity

## b. Lagged Endogenous Variables:

$X_{6it-1}$ = Quantity of exports of $i^{th}$ commodity demanded in $(t-1)^{th}$ period in thousand U.S. dollars.

$X_{7it-1}$ = Quantity of exports of $i^{th}$ commodity supplied in $(t-1)^{th}$ period in thousand U.S. dollars.

The general specification of the model was as follows:

### Exports of Coffee ($i$=1)

(Demand) $\qquad Y_{11t} = f(Y_{31t}, X_{11t}, X_{2t})$

(Supply) $\qquad Y_{21t} = f(Y_{31t}, X_{31t}, X_{4t}, X_{51})$

(Export market Equilibrium) $\qquad Y_{11t} = Y_{21t}$

### Exports of Tea ($i$=2)

(Demand) $\qquad Y_{12t} = f(Y_{32t}, X_{12t}, X_{2t})$

(Supply) $\qquad Y_{22t} = f(Y_{32t}, X_{32t}, X_{4t}, X_{52})$

(Export Market Equilibrium) $\qquad Y_{12t} = Y_{22t}$

### Exports of Basmati Rice ($i$=3)

(Demand) $\qquad Y_{13t} = f(Y_{33t}, X_{13t}, X_{3t})$

(Supply) $\qquad Y_{23t} = f(Y_{33t}, X_{33t}, X_{3t}, X_{53})$

(Export market Equilibrium) $\qquad Y_{13t} = Y_{23t}$

Linear form of export demand and export supply functions had been assumed for all the three commodities. For estimation purpose, the commodity wise actual specification of different models was as follows:

### Exports of Coffee ($i$=1)

(Demand) $\qquad Y_{11t} = a_{01} + a_{11}Y_{31t} + a_{21}X_{11t} + a_{31}X_{2t} + e_{11}$ $\qquad$ (3.4)

(Supply) $\qquad Y_{21t} = b_{01} + b_{11}Y_{31t} + b_{21}X_{31t} + b_{31}X_{4t} + b_{41}X_{51} + e_{21}$ $\quad$ (3.5)

(Export Market Equilibrium) $\qquad Y_{11t} = Y_{21t}$ (3.6)

### Exports of Tea ($i$=2)

(Demand) $\qquad Y_{12t} = a_{02} + a_{12}Y_{32t} + a_{22}X_{12t} + a_{32}X_{2t} + e_{12}$ $\qquad$ (3.7)

(Supply) $\qquad Y_{22t} = b_{02} + b_{12}Y_{32t} + b_{22}X_{32t} + b_{32}X_{4t} + b_{42}X_{52} + e_{22}$ $\quad$ (3.8)

(Export    Market    Equilibrium)                                      $Y_{12t}=Y_{22t}$

(3.9)

## Exports of Basmati Rice ($i$=3)

(Demand)                          $Y_{13t} = a_{03}+a_{13}Y_{33t}+a_{23}X_{13t}+a_{33}X_{2t}+e_{13}$        (3.10)

(Supply)                          $Y_{23t} =b_{03}+b_{13}Y_{33t}+b_{23}X_{33t}+b_{33}X_{4t}+b_{43}X_{53}+e_{23}$ (3.11)

(Export Market Equilibrium)    $Y_{13t}=Y_{23t}$                                    (3.12)

Where $e_1$, $e_2$ were two stochastic terms, $a_0$ and $b_0$ were the intercept and $a_{ji}$ and $b_{ji}$ were the regression coefficients associated with $j^{th}$ variable and $i^{th}$ commodity which were to be estimated.

In order to introduce the lag adjustment behaviour into the above models, exports were assumed to adjust to the difference between demand for exports in year t and actual flow in the previous year. Thus, the demand adjustment mechanism for export demand equation considered was:

$$\Delta Y_{1it}^{d}=K(Y_{1it}^{d}-Y_{1it-1}^{d})\ldots\ldots\ldots\ldots k>0$$

(3.13)

Where K was coefficient of demand adjustment and $\Delta Y_{1it}^{d}$ was a first difference operator,

$$\Delta Y_{1it}^{d} = Y_{1it}^{d} - Y_{1it-1}^{d}$$

Final export demand functions were derived by substituting equations (3.4, 3.7 and 3.10) into equation 3.13 and expressing the lagged endogenous variable as $X_{6it-1}$.

A similar supply adjustment mechanism for export supply equations was considered as follows:

$$\Delta Y_{2it}^{s}=Q(Y_{2it}^{s}-Y_{2it-1}^{s})\ldots\ldots\ldots\ldots Q>0$$                              (3.14)

Where Q was coefficient of supply adjustment, the final export supply function was derived by substituting equations (3.5, 3.8 and 3.10) into equation 3.14 and expressing the lagged endogenous variable as $X_{7it-1}$.

The adjustment function (3.14) assumed that the quantities of exports in a given year adjust to conditions of excess demand in the rest of the world, and therefore, the price of exports was determined in the exporting country.

For the case of supply adjustment function (3.14), it was assumed that the quantity of exports adjust to conditions of excess supply.

Specification of the model with lag adjustment behavior was as follows:

**Exports of Coffee ($i=1$)**

(Demand) $\quad Y_{11t}=Ka_{01}+Ka_{11}Y_{31t}+Ka_{21}X_{11t}+Ka_{31}X_{2t}+(1-K)X_{61t-1}+e_{11}$ $\qquad$ (3.15)

(Supply) $\qquad Y_{21t}=Qb_{01}+Qb_{11}Y_{31t}+Qb_{21}\ X_{31t}+Qb_{31}\ X_{4t}+Qb_{41}\ X_{51}+\ (1-Q)X_{71t-1}+e_{21}$

$\qquad\qquad\qquad\qquad\qquad\qquad\qquad\qquad\qquad\qquad\qquad\qquad$ (3.16)

(Export Market Equilibrium) $\qquad\qquad\qquad\qquad\qquad Y_{11t}=Y_{21t}$
(3.17)

**Exports of Tea ($i=2$)**

(Demand) $\qquad\qquad\qquad Y_{12t}=Ka_{02}+Ka_{13}Y_{32t}+Ka_{22}X_{12t}+Ka_{32}X_{2t}+\ (1-K)X_{62t-1}+e_{12}$
(3.18)

(Supply) $\qquad Y_{22t}=Qb_{02}+Qb_{12}Y_{32t}+Qb_{22}\ X_{32t}+Qb_{32}\ X_{4t}+Qb_{42}\ X_{52}+\ (1-Q)\ X_{72t-1}+e_{22}$

$\qquad\qquad\qquad\qquad\qquad\qquad\qquad\qquad\qquad\qquad\qquad\qquad$ (3.19)

(Export Market Equilibrium) $\qquad\qquad\qquad\qquad\qquad Y_{12t}=Y_{22t}$
(3.20)

**Exports of Basmati Rice ($i=3$)**

(Demand) $Y_{13t}=Ka_{03}+Ka_{13}Y_{33t}+Ka_{23}X_{13t}+Ka_{33}X_{2t}+\ (1-K)X_{63t-1}+e_{13}$ $\qquad$ (3.21)

(Supply) $\ Y_{23t}=Qb_{03}+Qb_{13}Y_{33t}+Qb_{23}\ X_{33t}+Qb_{33}\ X_{4t}+Qb_{43}\ X_{53}+\ (1-Q)X_{73t-1}+e_{23}$

$\qquad\qquad\qquad\qquad\qquad\qquad\qquad\qquad\qquad\qquad\qquad\qquad$ (3.22)

(Export Market Equilibrium) $\qquad\qquad\qquad\qquad\qquad Y_{13t}=Y_{23t}$
(3.23)

$\qquad$ The mean time lag in the adjustment of export demand was equal to $K^{-1}$ and could be calculated from the parameters of demand equation. Similarly the mean time lag in the adjustment of export supply was equal to $Q^{-1}$. All the equations were tested for identification and were found to be over identified. Therefore two stage least square model was used for the analysis.

$\qquad$ Problem of serial correlation (Autocorrelation): For the detection of presence of autocorrelation in the model, the Durbin Watson d-statistic was used. Although h- statistic is better for the detection of autocorrelation in case of lagged dependent variables, but Durbin Watson d- statistic was used due to its simple calculations and availability.

Null hypothesis:

$H_o$ : p equal to 0

And alternate hypothesis

$H_1$ : p not equal to 0 And first order autocorrelation was detected.

The Cocherane- Orcutt iterative procedure was used for the removal of this first order autocorrelation.

The various measures and ways to analyze the trade performance and its structure have been discussed in the previous sections. The results of the study are presented and analyzed in this section. This chapter starts with an overview of export and trends in the export of selected agricultural commodities from over the past two decades, followed by an overview of destination wise pattern of exports and then last but not least estimation of demand and supply functions for the export of selected agricultural commodities.

## 4.1    GROWTH RATE ANALYSIS AND INSTABILITY

Exports have played an increasingly important role in India's economic growth in the last two decades and created absolute gains for the trading partners involved and it served as the backbone of our modern commercial world as producers in various nations try to earn profit from an expanded market, rather than limited to selling within their own boundaries. The export of selected agricultural commodities namely tea, coffee and basmati rice from India in physical and value terms has been shown in table 4.1 and figure 4.1.

**Trend Analysis of Exports of Coffee, Tea and Basmati rice:**

Trend analysis is the practice of collecting information and attempting to spot a pattern, or trend, in the information. Trend analysis is often used to predict future events and it could be used to estimate uncertain events in the past. In order to assess the trend in export quantity and value of selected agricultural commodities for the period from 1990 to 2011, models like linear, logarithmic, inverse, quadratic, cubic, compound, power, S model, growth and exponential model, etc. were tried.

**A.)    Trend in Export Quantity of Coffee:**

Secondary data on export of coffee from India for the year 1990 to 2011 as published by FAO (table 4.1 and figure 4.1) show that export quantity has fluctuated between 80 thousand metric tons to about 2.40 lakh metric tones in the study period. The highest quantity of coffee was exported during the year 2011 and lowest was during the year 1990. In between these two years, export quantity of coffee showed a lot of variations. As depicted from the figure that export quantity of coffee from India had increased till 1996 but thereafter during 1997 a fall in exported quantity was observed and exported quantity became 136183 metric tones followed by increase in export quantity of coffee from

India during 1998 and 1999. Later on with rise and fall during the period 2001-2005 export quantity of coffee reached 188058 metric tones during 2006 followed by drastic fall till the year 2009. But during the years 2010, rise in exported quantity of coffee has been observed and exported quantity of coffee from India had reached 232572 metric tones which was highest exported quantity during study period.

**Table 4.1 Export of Selected agricultural commodities from India (1990-2011)**

| Year | Coffee | | Tea | | Basmati rice | |
|------|--------------------------|-------------------|--------------------------|-------------------|--------------------------|-------------------|
| | Quantity (metric tones) | Value ('000 US $) | Quantity (metric tones) | Value ('000 US $) | Quantity (metric tones) | Value ('000 US $) |
| 1990 | 82961 | 125683 | 198136 | 594191 | 217695 | 154045 |
| 1991 | 88796 | 116615 | 215144 | 490292 | 235590 | 177790 |
| 1992 | 107654 | 111305 | 166359 | 360933 | 286170 | 228341 |
| 1993 | 111043 | 137741 | 153159 | 331845 | 527233 | 338355 |
| 1994 | 120574 | 283955 | 150874 | 308399 | 442167 | 275613 |
| 1995 | 143795 | 369386 | 158333 | 359054 | 373314 | 254312 |
| 1996 | 146772 | 308935 | 138360 | 282579 | 523126 | 351447 |
| 1997 | 136183 | 344797 | 141972 | 497239 | 592678 | 453451 |
| 1998 | 179605 | 334292 | 201798 | 518258 | 597756 | 446139 |
| 1999 | 175830 | 264748 | 177507 | 406106 | 638379 | 410878 |
| 2000 | 161508 | 174622 | 200868 | 431596 | 851717 | 474156 |
| 2001 | 150943 | 151905 | 177603 | 367207 | 666713 | 391869 |
| 2002 | 164689 | 142590 | 181617 | 326629 | 710156 | 425533 |

| 2003 | 167495 | 157295 | 174246 | 333408 | 771475 | 442800 |
| 2004 | 140613 | 157109 | 174728 | 377742 | 1162989 | 629351 |
| 2005 | 157208 | 254586 | 159121 | 372628 | 1166562 | 687393 |
| 2006 | 188058 | 314660 | 181326 | 407375 | 1045714 | 619522 |
| 2007 | 152610 | 327897 | 193459 | 469274 | 1183355 | 1073796 |
| 2008 | 149624 | 372598 | 203207 | 590226 | 1556411 | 2060671 |
| 2009 | 126330 | 261526 | 203863 | 583803 | 2016775 | 2297285 |
| 2010 | 177926 | 379757 | 234560 | 694661 | 2370658 | 2491143 |
| 2011 | 232572 | 681121 | 322548 | 865427 | 3178174 | 3222311 |

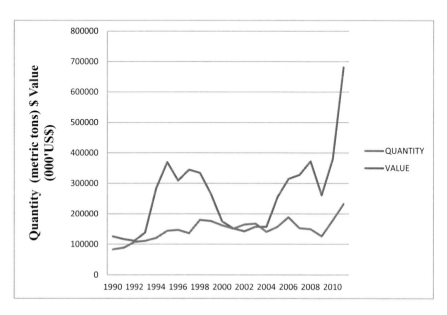

**Figure 4.1 Export of Coffee from India (1990-2011)**

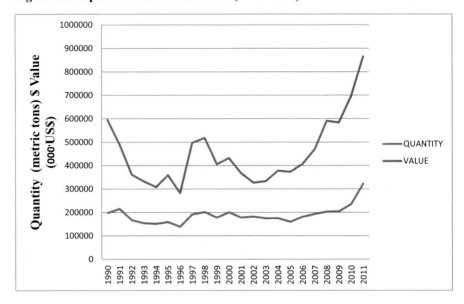

**Figure 4.2 Export of Tea from India (1990-2011)**

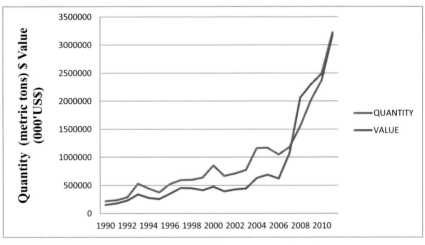

**Figure 4.3 Export of Basmati Rice from India (1990-2011)**

**Selection of best fit trend model for export quantity of coffee:**

The various trend models were fitted to coffee export data and judged with the help of value of coefficient of determination ($R^2$) and significance of it's coefficients. Power curve model was selected as the best fit model for export quantity of coffee from India as the $R^2$ value was found 0.70 whereas adjusted $R^2$ value was 0.69(Table 4.2). This means that almost 70 percent of the variation in export quantity of coffee can be explained by trend factor. The coefficients came out to be significant at 1% level of significance. This function has a shape like positive slope of concave below curve as value of p lies between 0 and 1. In future it may achieve a maxima and may become negative slope of concave below curve of power production function depending on the conditions. Graphical depiction of power curve model has been shown in figure 4.2. The curve is showing positive growth in the export quantity of coffee from India for the year 1990 to 2011. The parameter estimates significant at 1% level of significance of the power trend model for export quantity of coffee from India during 1990-2011 had been given in Table 4.2.

**Table 4.2 Best Estimated Trend Model of Export Quantity of Coffee**

| Model | Parameter Estimates | | $R^2$ | Adjusted $R^2$ |
|-------|---------------------|---|-------|----------------|
| Power | $Y = k\ X^p + u$ | | | |
| | Coefficient | 0.249* | 0.70 | 0.69 |
| | | (0.036) | | |

Note: * significant at 1% level of significance

Figures in the parenthesis shows the standard error value.

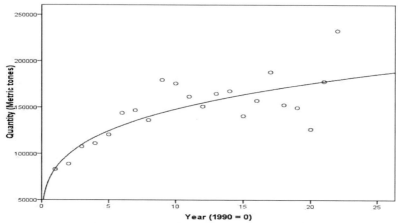

Figure 4.4: Growth trend (power) of export quantity of coffee

## B)    Trend for export value of coffee

In the international market effect of price can be observed from the particular commodity's value. So the trend in value of coffee was also analyzed. On the basis of secondary data of export value of coffee from India for the year 1990 to 2011 published by FAO, it could be stated that export value of coffee showed year to year fluctuation between 1990 and 2011 (Table 4.1 & Figure 4.1). Variation in export value of coffee could be due to variation in export quantity or its export price. The highest export value of exported coffee from India was observed during the year 2011 (681121 thousand US$) and lowest was during the year 1992 (111305 thousand US$). The lowest export value of coffee was due to fall in price of exported coffee during that year as there was no such change observed in the export quantity during that year. It can be depicted from the table that export value had increased to 344797 thousand US$ after 1992 till 1997 since demand of Indian coffee increased during these years followed by the fall in export till 2004. Later on export value of Indian coffee from India showed rise during the later years till 2011 which was the year of highest export of Indian coffee from India. This might be due to improved quality and increased demand of Indian coffee during these years.

### Selection of best fit trend model for export value of coffee:

For export of coffee in value terms several trend models like linear, cubic, quadratic, exponential, etc. were fitted. Cubic trend was selected as a best fit model as because its $R^2$ value was found better than other models. This model was showing parameter estimates significant at 1% level of significance. Thus trend factor was important in export value of coffee as the value of coffee export was being affected by export quantity variations from year to year and international price fluctuations. But cubic model was showing it's coefficients significant at 1% level of significance. Graphical depiction of cubic curve model has been shown in Figure 4.5. The curve has shown positive slope increasing at an increasing rate in the export value of coffee from India for the year 1990 to 2011. In future also, this curve may have a positive growth as cubic production function is always having growth of increasing slope at an increasing rate. The parameter estimates significant at 1% level of significance of the cubic trend model for export value of coffee from India during 1990-2011 had been given in Table 4.3.

**Table 4.3 Best Estimated Trend Model of Export Value of Coffee**

| Model | Parameter Estimates | $R^2$ | Adjusted $R^2$ |
|-------|---------------------|-------|----------------|
| Cubic | $Y = a+b_1x+b_2x^2+b_3x^3+u$ | 0.71 | 0.66 |
|       | $a = -52392.64 \ (78481.79)$ |  |  |
|       | $b_1 = 117202.77^* \ (28896.39)$ |  |  |
|       | $b_2 = -12567.26^* \ (2885.48)$ |  |  |
|       | $b_3 = 390.04^* \ \ \ (82.58)$ |  |  |

*Note: * significant at 1% level of significance*
*Figures in the parenthesis shows the standard error value.*

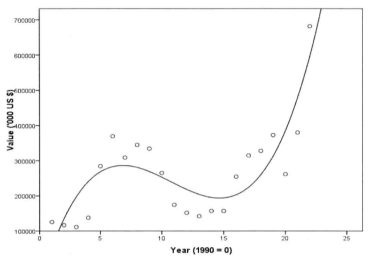

Figure 4.5: Cubic trend of export value of coffee

### C.) Trend in Export Quantity of Tea

Tea is very important agricultural commodity of India. The export quantity of tea from India for the year 1990 to 2011 was shown in Table 4.1. It can be depicted from the table that exported quantity of tea fluctuated around 200000 metric tons in last two decades. Graphical depiction of the export of quantity of tea can be from Figure: 4.2. The highest quantity of tea was exported during the year 2011 (322548 metric tons) and lowest was during the year 1996 (138360 metric tons).  As shown in Figure 4.2 that export quantity of tea increased during the initial years of our study period i.e. 1991 but after 1991 it fell down to 138360 metric tons till 1996 export during the year 1995 where it showed a slight increase. After that during the period 1996 to 2005 exported quantity of tea showed many fluctuations and drastically fell to 159121 metric tons during the year 2005. Later on after 2005 an increase in demand of Indian tea by importing countries was observed and export of tea significantly increased during the period 2006 to 2011 and reached to 322549 metric tons which was highest exported quantity of tea from of the study period i.e. 1990-2011.

### Selection of best fit trend model for Export Quantity of Tea

Various models had been tried to show the trend in exported quantity of tea but cubic model was selected as the best fit for export quantity of Tea from India during 1990-2011. $R^2$ value of this model was found 0.601 and adjusted $R_2$ value was 0.534 (Table 4.4) which was higher as compared to other models. It indicates that about 60 percent variation in exported quantity of tea from India can be explained by trend factor for the year 1990-2011. Only intercept of cubic trend was significant at 1% level of significance. This Graphical depiction of best fitted model i.e. cubic showing the trend for the export quantity of tea is done in Figure 4.6. the trend was like convex downward shape curve as the value of coefficient was more than zero and the trend was the increasing part of the curve and it seemed to be increase or decrease in future also. The parameter estimates has been shown in Table 4.4.

**Table 4.4 Best Estimated Trend Model of Export quantity of Tea:**

| Model | Parameter Estimates | | $R^2$ | Adjusted $R^2$ |
|-------|---------------------|---|-------|----------------|
| Cubic | $Y = a+b_1x+b_2x^2+b_3x^3+u$ | | 0.601 | 0.53 |
| | a = 178395.83* (26299.96) | | | |
| | $b_1$ = 3748.58 | (9683.44) | | |
| | $b_2$ = -908.62 | (966.95) | | |
| | $b_3$ = 42.703 | (27.675) | | |

*Note: * significant at 1% level of significance*
*Figures in the parenthesis shows the standard error value.*

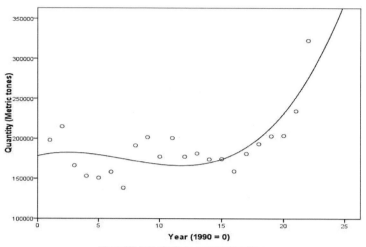

Figure 4.6: Cubic trend of export quantity of tea

## D.) Trend in Export Value of Tea:

Export value of tea followed a fluctuating trend between 1990 and 2011. There were more variation in value of tea exports than in quantity of exports. This means that international prices of tea were more volatile (Table 4.1). The highest export value of tea exported from India was observed during the year 2011 (865427 thousand US$) and lowest was during the year 1996 (282579 thousand US$). The lowest export value of tea was due to fall in quantity of export of tea during that year. It can be depicted from the table that export value had fell down to 282579 thousand US $ till 1996 since export quantity of tea also fell down during these years followed by rise till1998. Later on export value of Indian tea showed slight variation during the period 1999 to 2009. Thereafter increase in value of export was observed during the years 2010-11. This might be due to improved quality and increased quantity of exported tea during these years as well as higher prices received due to improvement in quality of Indian tea in later years.

### Selection of best fit trend model for export value of tea

Cubic model was selected as the best fit one among all the models that were used to model the trend, as it provided highest $R^2$ value i.e 0.71 for trend in export value of tea from India as shown in Table4.5. The other models have also been tried but didn't show the best results as the $R^2$ value was lesser than this model. The $R^2$ value of this model indicates that 71% of variation explained by trend factor in export value of tea. Parameter estimates can be concluded from table 4.5. Trend is shown in Figure 4.7. the intercept of this function was significant at 1% level of significance. This function was having a shape like convex downward shape curve as coefficient were more than zero. Figure 4.7 showed that this was the increase part of the trend and it seemed to increase in future.

**Table: 4.5: Best Estimated Trend Model of Export Value of Tea**

| Model | Parameter Estimates | $R^2$ | Adjusted $R^2$ |
|-------|--------------------|-------|----------------|
| Cubic | $Y = a+b_1x+b_2x^2+b_3x^3+u$ | **0.71** | **0.66** |
|  | $a = 480769.82*$ (84342.84) |  |  |
|  | $b_1 = -6446.08$ (31054.38) |  |  |
|  | $b_2 = -1968.65$ (3100.96) |  |  |
|  | $b_3 = 132.69$ (88.752) |  |  |

Note:  * indicate significance at 1 per cent level.

Figures in the parenthesis shows the standard error value.

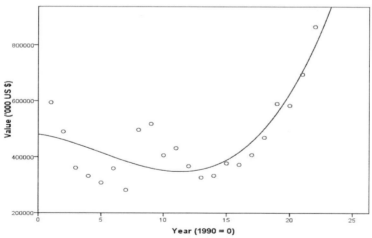

Figure 4.7: Cubic trend of export value of tea

**E.)    Trend in Export Quantity of Basmati rice:**

53

India is one of the largest producer and exporter of basmati rice in the world. Export of Indian basmati rice started in early 1990's and nearly two thirds of basmati rice produced in India was used for export. Between 1990-2011 export quantity of basmati rice fluctuated between 2 lakh metric tones to about 31 lakh metric tones as shown in Table 4.1 & Figure 4.3. In the year 1990 India exported 217695 metric tones of basmati rice. Since then the export of basmati rice from India has increased consistently over the years. In 2011 India exported 3178174 metric tones of basmati rice. Thus, Indian basmati rice had made its own unique position over the entire world and fetched good export price in the international market because of its super fine grain, pleasant aroma and extreme grain elongation. Only During 1995, 2001 and 2006 the export of basmati rice from India showed a slight dip otherwise export of the basmati rice from India had increased throughout the study period. Although basmati rice exports from India show a positive growth over the years, there is strong competition from Pakistan's Basmati, USA' Texamati and Thialand's Siamati in the world market.

**Selection of best fit trend model for export quantity of Basmati Rice**

Exponential model was selected as the best fit model for export quantity of basmati rice from India. Exponential trend is significant at 1% level of significance and $R^2$ value was found to be 0.93 as shown in Table4.6. This indicated that almost 93 percent of the variation in export quantity of basmati rice could be explained by trend factor. Graphical depiction of exponential model is shown in figure-4.8. The curve is showing positive growth in the export quantity of basmati rice from India for the year 1990 to 2011. The coefficients for this function were significant at 1% level of significance and the shape for it showed that export quantity of basmati rice was increasing at an increasing rate and it seemed to be increase in future also.

**Table: 4.6 Best Estimated Trend Model of Export Quantity of Basmati rice:**

| Model | Parameter Estimates | | $R^2$ | Adjusted $R^2$ |
|---|---|---|---|---|
| **Exponential** | $Y = e^x + u$ | | 0.93 | 0.927 |
| | Coefficient | 0.106* | | |
| | | (0.006) | | |

*Note: * significant at 1% level of significance*

*Figures in the parenthesis shows the standard error value.*

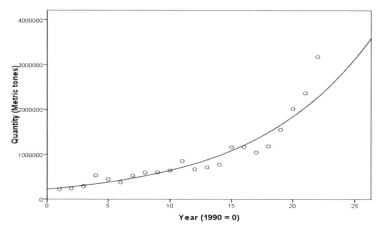

Figure 4.8: Exponential trend of export quantity of basmati rice

## F.)    Trend in Export Value of Basmati Rice:

Value of any commodity depicts the price effect on any commodity's quantity. Tabular depiction of export value of basmati rice exports from India (Table 4.1and Figure 4.3) show that the basmati rice exports in value terms have not been fluctuated a lot between 1990 and 2011. The highest export value was observed during the year 2011 (3222311 thousand US$) and lowest was during the year 1990 (154045.9 thousand US$). Like export quantity it also followed the same trend, this showed that export price had not imposed large impact on export value of basmati rice from India. During the years 1996, 2001 and 2005-06 it slipped down and showed fluctuation due to the fall in exported quantity of basmati rice and during the year 2011 the export value reached to 3222311 thousand US$ which was a significant figure in terms of export of basmati rice.

### Selection of best fit trend model for export value of Basmati rice

The exponential model was the best fit one as it provided highest $R^2$ value for trend in export value of basmati rice from India. The $R^2$ value was 0.86 as can be seen from Table4.7. Figure 4.9 is showing the trend in export value of basmati rice from India. The value of $R^2$ indicated that about 86% of the variation in export value of basmati rice from India could be explained by the trend factor for the period 1990 - 2011. The coefficients were significant at 1% level of significant. The shape of the trend was shown in figure 4.9 which explained the increased export value of basmati rice at an increasing rate. It seemed to increase at increasing rate in future also as exponential function is always having a shape like this as shown in the figure.

**Table 4.7 Best Estimated Trend Model of Export Value of Basmati rice:**

| Model | Parameter Estimates | | $R^2$ | Adjusted $R^2$ |
|---|---|---|---|---|
| **Exponential** | $Y = e^x + u$ | | 0.86 | 0.85 |
| | Coefficient | 0.12* | | |
| | | (0.011) | | |

Note: * significant at 1% level of significance.

*Figures in the parenthesis shows the standard error value.*

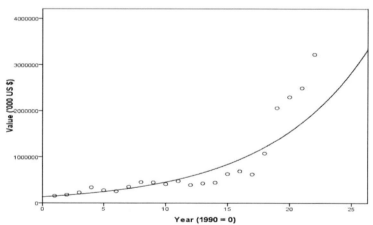

Figure 4.9: Exponential trend of export value of basmati rice

### 4.1.1. Growth Rate Analysis

Growth rate indicates the amount of increase that a specific variable has gained within a specific period and context. Growth rate of export of three commodities namely coffee, tea and basmati rice has been analyzed in this section. The compound annual growth rates presented in Table 4.8 revealed that basmati rice witnessed the highest growth rate (11.14%), followed by coffee (2.76%) and tea (1.37%) during the 1990-2011. The main reason for significant

56

growth in export of basmati rice during the study period was that India was able to maintain its unique position as producer of good quality aromatic basmati rice in the international market.

During 1990-91, the coffee exports from India were 82961 metric tones. In the span of 11 years (1990-2011) coffee exports increased by almost three folds (232572 metric tons). Coffee registered quantity wise annual growth rate of 2.76% whereas value wise growth rate was 4.29 % during 1990-2011. This showed that during the study period, rise in value of coffee was higher than the growth in quantity exported over the years.

Now taking tea into consideration which is traditional export commodity of India. Export of tea from India was analyzed and compound growth rate has been calculated according to which growth rate of tea in quantity terms was1.37 % per annum and in value terms growth rate was 2.04 % per annum. This means that per year tea exports are growing by 1.37% in quantity terms and 2.04% in value terms. In quantum Indian tea exports recorded a rise from 198136 metric tones valued at Rs. 594191 thousand $ during 1990-91 and increased to 322548 metric tones valued at Rs. 865427 thousand $ in 2010-11.

A positive growth rate of basmati rice represents a growing export market as given in table 4.8.Last but very important commodity basmati rice which is having important position among exported agricultural commodities from India, quantity wise growth rate of basmati rice export from India were 11.14 % during 1990-2011 and in terms of value growth rate was 12.97 % during 1990-2011. This means that per year basmati exports from India are growing by 11.14% in quantity terms and 12.97% in value terms. In absolute terms, the quantum of Indian basmati rice recorded a rise from 217695 metric tones in 1990-91 to 3178174 metric tones in 2010-11 whereas in value terms it recorded a growth of 15404 thousand $ during 1990-91 to 3222311 thousand $ during 2010-11 (Table: 4.1). Thus, among the three commodities selected in this study basmati rice had highest growth rate as it remained a principal exported commodity of India.

**Table 4.8 Compound Growth Rate for Export of Selected Agricultural Commodities (1990-2011)**

**(% per annum)**

| Commodity | Quantity | Value |
|-----------|----------|-------|
| **Coffee** | 2.76 | 4.29 |

| Tea | 1.37 | 2.04 |
|---|---|---|
| **Basmati Rice** | 11.14 | 12.97 |

### 4.1.2 Instability Analysis:

Agriculture sector is prone to risk and uncertainty and measuring the growth coupled with instability is important so as to assess the real improvement in agricultural parameters in the past. It is important to have quantitative measures of instability, so that the seriousness of the problem can be assessed objectively.

In order to study the variation in the export trade of agricultural commodities of India, an attempt was made to analyze the instability in the export of agricultural commodities over the period 1990-2011. The deterministic component of the total variability in exports was calculated by analyzing arithmetic deviation of exports from actual trend ($I_1$) and by fitting an exponential trend and then taking coefficient of variation ($I_2$). The coefficient of variation is a statistical measure to assess the extent of variation in a set of data. As far as inter year extent of variation in the export of crops is concerned, the coefficient of variation of original export data may include trend, cyclical variation, seasonal variation and irregular or random variation. Among all the selected commodities, i.e., coffee, tea and basmati rice, basmati rice emerged with high Coefficient of Variation values for export quantity as well as for value as shown in the Table 4.9. The basmati rice was showing the highest value for both export quantity and value by both the measures.

The coefficient of variation with respect to export quantity of coffee was observed to be 15.73% while taking deviation from trend as a measure of instability it was found to be 23.05% instable during the study period (1990-2011) as shown in Table : 4.9. Similarly deviation from the trend with respect to export value of coffee was 50.52% whereas by taking coefficient of variation into consideration it was found to be 41.20% during the study period (1990-2011), it showed a relatively high instability in exports in value terms as compared to quantity of coffee due to high fluctuation in price during whole study period i.e. 1990-2011.

In case of tea, the instability of export quantity while taking arithmetic deviation into consideration was 19.95% during 1990-2011 whereas its coefficient of variation was found to be 16.87 % during the study period. It showed lesser instability during 1990-2011 study period. Also instability w. r. t.

export value of tea was 31.53% and 28.29% by taking deviation from the trend and coefficient of variation, respectively during 1990-2011 as shown in Table 4.9. The study results showed that during 1990-2011 there was more variation in value of export as compared to the quantity of export due to high fluctuations in prices of tea.

The instability during the study period 1990-2011 with respect to export quantity of basmati rice was observed to be 77.46 % whereas its coefficient of variation was found to be 182.80 % and in terms of value of export it was 106.43% and 281.09%, respectively as shown in Table 4.9. This showed that export value remained highly unstable as compared to export quantity during 1990-2011 due to more fluctuations in price. The result represented that there was more instability in basmati rice as compared to other two commodities under study i.e. tea and coffee that was due to the reason that basmati rice had an increased trend of export in both quantity as well as in value terms since 1990-2011. This may be due to the fluctuating demand of Indian basmati rice because of competitive nature of the commodity in the world foreign exchange market.

**Table 4.9    Instability in quantitative and value export of different commodities in India (1990-2011)**

| Commodity | | $I_1$ | $I_2$ |
|---|---|---|---|
| **Coffee** | Quantity | 23.05 | 15.73 |
| | Value | 50.52 | 41.20 |
| **Tea** | Quantity | 19.95 | 16.87 |
| | Value | 31.53 | 28.29 |
| **Basmati Rice** | Quantity | 77.46 | 182.81 |
| | Value | 106.43 | 281.09 |

*Note: $I_1$: deviation from the trend.*
*Note: $I_2$: coefficient of variation.*

## IDENTIFICATION OF CROPS ACCORDING TO PATTERN OF INSTABILITY

The description of trend, growth rate and instability would help to assess the past performance of export of crops. Generally the Coefficient of variation values more than 30 is considered as high in agriculture. Classification of crops in terms of growth and instability in export performance are given in table 4.10 and table 4.11.

The export quantity of Tea and coffee were having lower value as compared to the basmati rice as shown in the table 4.10. This shows that the export of tea and coffee was highly stable and acceptable during the study period. This may be due to increased demand of tea and coffee by the importers while the basmati rice indicated an unacceptable deviation from the trend in terms of export quantity which shows the high fluctuation in the export of basmati rice. Taking export in value terms higher level of fluctuations were shown by coffee, tea and basmati rice which indicated that there was higher level of instability as measured by deviation from the trend as shown in table 4.10.

**Table 4.10   Classification of selected crops in terms of instability (deviation from the trend) in the Export Quantity and value terms from India (1990-2011)**

| Instability | Quantity terms | Value terms |
|---|---|---|
| **High (> 30%)** | Basmati Rice. | Coffee, Basmati Rice, Tea |
| **Low (< 30%)** | Tea and Coffee | |

Now taking coefficient of variation as the measure of instability export quantity of tea and coffee were found to stable due to less than 30% coefficient of variation as these commodities were tradition exported commodities of India whereas the export quantity of basmati rice was most unstable due to fluctuations in the demand of Indian Basmati rice. Export value of coffee and basmati rice explained more instability as the value of coefficient of variation was more than 30% due to unstable price level as compared to export value of tea which was stable due to lower value of instability and having a stable demand in the world as shown in the Table 4.11.

**Table 4.11: Classification of selected crops in terms of instability (coefficient of variation) in the Export Quantity and value terms from India (1990-2011)**

| Instability | Quantity terms | Value terms |
|---|---|---|
| **High (> 30%)** | Basmati Rice | Coffee, Basmati Rice |
| **Low (< 30%)** | Tea and Coffee | Tea |

## 4.2 PATTERN OF DESTINATION

To study the performance of exports of any commodity, two things are important- one is change in exported quantity overtime and other is changes in destination of it's exports. Thus, study of pattern of exports of commodity overtime and over space, both are important. In international trade, trading partners are decided through demand and supply dimensions, multilateral agreements and domestic and international policies leading to comparative advantages. Composition of India's agricultural export has been changing over time. The selected commodities namely tea, coffee and basmati rice played an important role in agricultural exports and the changes in the pattern of their export took place due to various reasons. Export has produced economic benefits deriving from efficiency gains associated with exploiting comparative advantages and improved allocation of scarce resources. There are also dynamic gains in export sector driven by greater competition, greater economies of scale, better use of capacity, dimensions of knowledge and technological progress. To be export competitive among countries with similar resource endowments, a range of supporting domestic policies were required. Many countries are unable to realize the full potential of export led growth because domestic preconditions remain largely unfulfilled. For example, least developed countries still contribute just 1% to global trade. Partial efforts have been made by many countries, but anything short of a comprehensive approach fails to overcome the full range of constraints inhibiting export development.

Agricultural markets all over the world are characterized by government interventions of varied forms. The peculiarities associated with the agricultural sector made the governments to intervene at different stages of production, marketing and consumption of agricultural commodities. The interventions were made through direct measures like provisioning of subsidies in input and output markets, or through indirect measures like control of external trade with tariff or non-tariff barriers. With the Agreement on Agriculture (AoA) in the Uruguay Round of GATT /WTO, an attempt was made to formalize the removal or reduction of these interventions, which distort the agricultural markets. The rules and regulations governing agricultural trade covered in the clauses of AoA required the nontariff barriers to be converted to tariffs, reduction of tariffs over a period of time, and reduction of subsidies to production and exports of agricultural commodities. Agricultural policies now are therefore, governed by the rules under the WTO. In India too, government interventions in agricultural markets are seen in many forms, like fixation of support prices, procurement of marketed surplus for the public distribution to the consumers, maintenance of buffer stocks, provision of input subsidies, imposition of restrictions on movement of products and control on external trade in inputs and outputs through the tariffs and quantitative restrictions (QRs). Liberalization in external trade was one of the main packages of the New Economic Reforms in 1991. Though agriculture was not vastly covered under these policies, the impact of other policy measures towards this sector cannot be neglected (Rao, 1995). It is seen earlier that agriculture has not remained unaffected by the reform measures in the country, as the indirect impacts of liberalization of the economy in general and on agriculture in particular is far more important than the impacts of liberalization measures directly affecting this sector (Parikh, et al,. 1995). In addition, there were measures towards liberalization in external trade in agriculture from mid nineties, to meet the internal requirements, and in the late nineties, to meet the requirements under the WTO. These measures have direct impact on trade in agriculture. Thus, given the nature of liberalization and that of agriculture in India, the impact of liberalization policies at different phases on different agricultural commodities would be quite varied. The impact of such changes would also be felt at a macro level on related variables like the trade balance, the terms of trade, the level of prices and growth in agriculture and in the economy. Examining the changes in incentives/protection given to agricultural commodities and analyzing the implications of liberalization measures for agricultural sector and the economy in general, are relevant in this context.

For the better understanding of the export performance of selected agricultural commodities namely coffee, tea and basmati rice from India, the destination of their exports were studied overtime and changes in them were analyzed.

The total quantity of coffee exported from India during 2010-11 including re-exported coffee after value addition was 2,95,344 Metric Tons. The coffee exports during 2010-11 has been the highest as compared to the previous record of exports of 2,49,029 Metric Tons during the year 2006-07.The major top ten importing countries for coffee from India between 2001 to 2011 were Italy, Germany, Belgium, Spain, Slovenia, Greece, Algeria, Australia, Saudi Arabia and Jordan. Together these ten countries accounted for about 78% of our total coffee exports in the year 2011. Italy, Germany and Belgium were three most important consistent importers of coffee from India during 2001-2011 (Table 4.12). They consistently remained at first three positions of importing countries of India while the countries from fourth to tenth rank changed their imported quantity of coffee from India year to year. Italy which was the top most importer throughout the study period, imported 37,422 metric tons of coffee from India during 2001.

Imported quantity increased during 2002-03 followed by slight fall during 2004 and then again import of coffee by Italy increased during the year 2006 followed by slight ups and downs during the period 2007-10 and lastly, it maintained its top most rank with the import quantity of 64,401 metric tons of coffee from India. Similarly, Germany was the second most important export destination of coffee from India. Germany imported 28,546 metric tons of coffee during first year of study period i.e. 2001 but import of coffee by the country fell down constantly upto 2005 then it again increased its import quantity and imported 26,109 metric tons of coffee from India in 2006. During 2009 there was a sudden decline in its imports to 9,635 metric tons of coffee from India. During last three years the country made improvements and started importing more quantity of coffee from India and during last year of study period it imported 37,769 metric tons and maintained its second position. The third important country as stated above was Belgium which was an important trading partner in coffee export from India during the study period. Between 2001 and 2011, Belgium has maintained its third position in major importing countries of coffee from India with some year to year variations. U.S.A was also important importer of coffee from India during 2001-2004. It was at fourth rank during 2001 then it slipped down to sixth rank and it had lost its position among top ten importing countries of coffee from India after 2005. This might be due to the reason that in U.S.A. during 2005-06 there was overproduction of coffee along with under consumption and market oligopoly conditions which made U.S.A. self sufficient for its coffee demand (Bacon, 2004). The other export markets for coffee from India included countries like Spain, Slovenia and Greece which maintained their positions among top ten major importers except slight variations in their ranks. Newly emerging importers of coffee from India included countries like Algeria, Jordan, Egypt, Crotia, Australia, Kuwait, Israel, Saudi Arabia, etc during 2007-11. These countries replaced Netherland, Switzerland, Japan, France, Portugal, Russian Federation who were among leading importers during 2001-06. According to Coffee Exporters' Association of India, sluggish demand from Europe following the economic slump might be the reason for the declining demand of European countries for Indian Coffee after 2006.

The principal tea producing countries of the world are India, China, Sri Lanka, Kenya and Indonesia. These five countries account for 76% of world production and 79% of the tea exports, respectively. India is the largest producer and consumer of black tea in the world. Tea exports bring in important foreign exchange into the country; the sector also contributed revenue to the tea growing states and national exchequer by way of Value Added Tax, agricultural and corporate income tax, etc. India exported 322548 metric tones of tea to the different countries demanding tea from India during 2010-11. The top ten importing countries of tea from India during 2001-11 were Russian Federation, U.A.E., United Kingdom, Iraq, Kazakhstan, U.S.A., Iran, Germany, Pakistan and Australia. Russian Federation, U.A.E. and United Kingdom were top three export destinations of Indian tea throughout the study period (Table 4.13). Russian Federation was the leading importer country of tea from India since 2001 to 2011 with import of 67,007 metric tons of tea from India during 2001. But there was continuous fall in the imported quantity upto 2005. During 2006 to 2008 there were variations in quantity imported by Russian Federation. After 2008 the imports of tea by Russian Federation from India have consistently increased. During 2011 export quantity of tea from India to Russian Federation was 46,443 metric tons which made it to secure its position at second rank and Tunisia appeared as top most importer country of tea from India in 2011 that was due to large demand of orthodox – black & green tea in Tunisia and increased growth in off trade value so to regulate the supply and demand of tea in the country (57th Annual report 2010-11). A major factor affecting Indian tea exports during 2011 year was on account of lower exports to Russian Federation due to increased competition from other producer countries. United

Arab Emirates, the second most important importer of Indian tea imported 21,917 metric tons of tea from India in 2001. Then in 2002 it was replaced by Iraq and it slipped down to third position although its import quantity increased. Thereafter, it regained its rank as second highest importing country of tea from India during the year 2003 to 2005. After 2005 to till 2011, it has remained a major importer of tea from India with small year to year variations. United Kingdom the other most important export destination of tea from India maintained its third rank during the study period except during 2002, where it slipped down to fourth rank replaced by United Arab Emirates and 2008, where it raised its rank to second position replacing United Arab Emirates. The other export markets of Indian Tea were Kazakhstan, United States of America and Iran which remained among top ten importers. The countries like Poland, Japan, Sudan, etc. imported tea in earlier years but now they were not our leading destinations. The newly emerging export market in case of tea included countries like Saudi Arabia, Tunisia, Afghanistan, Srilanka, Egypt, etc.

The increase in export of tea from India during 2006-07 was largely due to increased off take by countries like Iraq, Afghanistan, Kenya, Pakistan and Egypt. In fact, the increase in exports to Pakistan had been quite substantial. Markets such as Russia, United Kingdom, Egypt, United Arab Emirates and Pakistan continued to be of vital importance because keeping with the requirements of the export and domestic markets, there was a focus on quality in a sustained manner. A marginal improvement was also noticed in the countries like Ireland and Iran during 2006-07 as compared to the corresponding period of 2005-06. During 2006-07 there was decline in exports to some of the countries including Russia, United Arab Emirates, United Kingdom, United States of America, Iran. In addition, decline in exports to Germany, Canada, Poland, Saudi Arabia, Singapore, Japan, Sri Lanka and Australia was also noticed. The decline in exports during 2010-11 was due to low purchase of tea by Russian Federation, Iraq, Afghanistan, United Kingdom, and Egypt as compared to last year. Exports to Afghanistan and Iraq suffered a setback due to the unstable situation there (Annual report 2011).

The leading aromatic fine quality rice in world trade popularly known as Basmati rice is fetching good export price in the international markets for its three distinct quality features viz.-pleasant aroma, superfine grains and extreme grain elongation. India is a major producer of basmati rice and accounts for almost 70% of the world production and nearly two-third of the country's produce is exported. During the study period (2001-11) the major consumer countries of Indian basmati rice were Saudi Arabia, United Arab Emirates, Iran, Kuwait, United States of America, Yemen, Belgium, Canada and Netherland. India's basmati rice exports stood at a record 31,78,174 tons in 2011 against 6,66,713 tons in 2001. Destination wise pattern of export of basmati rice can be concluded from (Table 4.14). Which shows that Saudi Arabia constantly remained as top most importer of basmati rice upto 2009 and during 2010 & 2011 it slipped down to second position. It imported 4,06,096 metric tons of basmati rice from India during 2001 which increased to 7,21,245 metric tons in 2011. Kuwait, the second important country importing Basmati rice from India during 2001 imported 65257.26metric tons of basmati rice from India. Its basmati rice import have increased to 1,99,868 metric tons in 2011. United Kingdom, United States of America, United Arab Emirates and Yemen were also important importing countries of basmati rice from India between 2001 and 2011. It is clear that India had a consolidated market for its basmati rice exports. It had consistent long term trading partners during the whole study period. Some diversifications in the basmati rice export market for India was seen after 2005 in the form of inclusion of new countries as importers. These were new destinations which India had tapped and these prospective markets included Middle Asian countries like Iran, Iraq, Qatar, Oman and Jordan and East Asian countries like Singapore. Out of these Iran and Iraq seemed promising markets for basmati rice exports from India. Iran served as third largest importer of basmati rice from India since 2008 as India restarted direct shipments of basmati rice to Iran with the new payment mechanism allowing the Iranian traders to make payment in Indian rupee. Due to the United States and European Union sanctions against Iran, the direct shipment from India was not possible so the Indian traders had to export basmati rice to Iran through third country like United Arab Emirates, etc. But with new bilateral payment mechanism, the payment transactions were done directly through banks. And the traders also expected that, with the direct shipments, the exports moved up by 10-15% this year as the direct exports reduced the logistics costs for importers and eventually increased the quantity. It is the quality of Indian basmati rice which had maintained a large consumer base worldwide. Commercial conditions were also good for increasing India's exports. India was no longer worried about having enough rice for its own people. Rice stocks of basmati and non basmati combined had surpassed targets of 12.2m tones to reach 32.1m tones during 2012 (Directorate of rice development, Patna).

**Share of importing countries in total export of coffee, tea and basmati rice**

Indian agricultural commodities have come to occupy a supreme position in the global market over the years. Today, India is a major supplier of several agricultural commodities like tea, coffee, rice, spices, cashew, oil meals, fresh fruits, fresh vegetables, meat and its preparations and marine products to the international market. Exports from any country plays very important role in the overall development of that country. The demand and supply situations in the Asian continent have undergone a rapid transformation due to the growth of the world economy and lowering of trade barriers (Aksoy and Beghin, 2005). An economic upheaval which took place in most of the South-East Asian countries has resulted in the creation of a huge supply potential in these economies along with an increase in their per capita income and a simultaneous increase in their trade potential. Indian economy in itself has undergone a rapid transformation after the inception of economic reforms in 1991. India's ratification of the Agreement on Agriculture (AoA) with WTO also had a major impact leading to redefining of its agricultural trade. During this time span, various agricultural commodities exported from India have responded differently and their levels of comparative advantage in the global markets have altered significantly. For India, agriculture serves as an important sector which has significant share in country's GDP and contributes major share in total exports from India. Coffee, tea and basmati rice were among major exported agricultural commodities from India.

An attempt has been made to study the share of imports of different countries from India at three points of time 2001, 2006 and 2011 for selected commodities of coffee, tea and basmati rice. Coffee, one of the major exported agricultural commodities, has large demand all over the world due its superior quality and safety parameters. The transitional probability, presented in Figure 4.10, 4.11 and 4.12 for the year 2001, 2006 &2011, respectively depicts a broad idea of change in direction of coffee export from India. It can be concluded from Figure 4.10, 4.11and 4.12 that shares of different importer countries of Indian coffee from India were varying with the period of time. In total India had exported 232572 metric tons of coffee to the world. The topmost importing countries of coffee from India were Italy, Germany, Belgium and Spain. Italy remained a leading importer of coffee from India during the year 2001, 2006 & 2011 which imported 25%, 33% & 28% of India's total coffee export, respectively followed by Germany which was 19%, 14% and 16%, respectively with respect to coffee export from India during these selected periods of time (Figure 4.10, 4.11 & 4.12). Belgium was also one of the major importers of coffee from India. It was on third position consistently during the study period. It can be seen from the figure that United States of America was not stable importer of coffee from India, even though around 8% of the total coffee export from India was imported by United States of America in 2001 but later on export of coffee from India to this nation was reduced due to reduced demand of Indian coffee and as a result of which it had lost its share to other countries like Saudi Arabia, Australia, Jordan, Algeria, etc. during 2011. The countries like Cambodia, Canada, Iraq, Iran, etc. pooled under other countries category had 26% of retention of total coffee exports from India during 2011 which was 23% during 2006 and 12% during 2001 it implied that retention of countries pooled under other category gained its share in total coffee export from India over the study period.

Tea, a traditionally exported agricultural commodity from India has its own importance in total agricultural exports. During 2001 and 2011 India had exported 198136 metric tons and 322548 metric tons of tea, respectively. In the world scenario, the effects of the liberalized regime of imports under WTO obligations and freeing of tea imports among SAARC countries apart from India's Free Trade Agreement with Sri Lanka on preferential Tariff terms increased competition in international markets, developments affecting Indian exports in countries such as Russia, Libya, Egypt etc. combined with declining prices of tea in Indian auctions, continued to provide a serious challenge to the Indian tea industry, during the year under review. Persual of data from Figure 4.13 with respect to tea export reveals that Russian Federation was on top position during 2001 consuming major share of 38% of total tea export from India which declined to 18% of the total tea export from India during the year 2006 but still it maintained it's top position but the share of Russian Federation declined drastically to 14% during the year 2011. As a result of which it slipped down to second position. Import trend by Russian Federation was in decreasing order during the study period. During 2011, Tunisia emerged as major importer of tea from India and imported about 21% of total tea export from India which was significantly higher over all the other importer countries. Contribution of United Arab Emirates during 2001 was 12%, which later on it was decreased to 10% during the years 2006 & 2011. United Kingdom was also among one of the major export market of Indian tea with the contribution of 10% during the year 2011 which was earlier 15% during 2006 & 12% of total tea exports from India during the year 2001, respectively. The other importing countries of Indian tea were Iran, Kazakhstan, United States of America, etc. during the study period.

Further it was noticed that during 2001, Pakistan was among one of the other importer countries of tea from India. But later it increased the Indian tea import and the share of Pakistan was significantly increased to 7% & 8% during the year 2006 & 2011, respectively. Iraq was also major importer of tea from India during 2001 with the share of 9% of tea export from India which reduced to only 5% during 2006 and during 2011, its share reduced drastically and hence it was clubbed under other importing countries of Indian tea. While the countries pooled under other countries group have percentage share of 20% in total tea export from India during the year 2011 which was 26% during 2006 and 1% which was drastically low during 2001 ( Figure 4.13, 4.14 &4.15).

Basmati, the unique aromatic quality rice, is a nature's gift to Indian sub-continent. The steady increase in production, availability of buffer stocks and the growing demand for basmati rice in the international market made India as an important rice exporting country of the world. Basmati rice captures higher returns as it is priced three times higher (US$ 800-1200 per metric ton) over non basmati rice (US $ 200-400 per metric tons) in the international as well as in the domestic markets. About 50-70% of basmati produced in the country is exported mainly to Saudi Arabia (68%), UAE, UK, Kuwait and others (Rani *et.al.*, 2011). In total India had exported 3178174 metric tons of basmati rice to various countries. Assessment of data from figure 3 indicates that major basmati rice importer countries were Saudi Arabia, Kuwait, United Kingdom, United Arab Emirates, etc. during the study period i.e. 2001-2011 and export to remaining minor importer countries were pooled under other countries. Saudi Arabia remained consistently as top most importer of Indian basmati rice during 2001-11. It can be seen from the figure that it remained as leading importer of basmati rice followed by United Arab Emirates & Iran during the year 2011. Saudi Arabia imported more than half i.e. 61% of the total basmati rice export from India during 2001 and nearly half i.e. 48% of total basmati rice exported from India during 2006. However, fluctuation in the share were observed over time. Export of Indian basmati rice from India to Saudi Arabia was later on drastically reduced to only one fourth which was 23% of total basmati rice exported from India during 2011. During 2001, the major importing countries were Saudi Arabia, Kuwait & United Kingdom whereas during 2006 major export markets were Saudi Arabia as consistent leading importer, Kuwait as second major importer and United Arab Emirates as third one. In 2001 & 2006, share of Kuwait in total basmati rice export from India during the respective years was around 10% of total basmati rice exported from India but later on during 2011 it decreased in its share was observed, with the emergence of Iran & United Arab Emirates as leading importer countries of Basmati Rice from India which imported 19% & 23%, respectively, of total basmati rice export from India. Iran emerged as major importer country during the year 2011 due to the new bilateral payment mechanism (Figure 4.16, 4.17 & 4.18).

This study shows that with the emergence of new markets for Indian agricultural commodities the prospects for growth and development of our international trade has significantly increased. It is important to maintain quality standard of the exportable commodities, adoption of policies that will improve the trade relationships of our nation with other countries of the world and to reduce our export barriers.

## 4.3 DEMAND AND SUPPLY FUNCTION OF SELECTED COMMODITIES OF INDIAN AGRICULTURAL EXPORTS

Indian agricultural commodities have come to occupy a supreme position in the global market over the years. Today, India is a major supplier of several agricultural commodities like tea, coffee, rice, spices, cashew, oil meals, fresh fruits, fresh vegetables, meat and its preparations and marine products to the international market. However, the country faces fierce competition from other major players in the field, both the existing and new entrants in the fray. Ironically, the major challenge is from within Asia itself where countries like China, Malaysia, Philippines, Thailand, Singapore and Indonesia among others pose a big threat to Indian agricultural products export. The demand and supply situations in the Asian continent have under gone a rapid transformation due to the growth of the world economy and lowering of trade barriers (Aksoy and Beghin, 2005). Indian economy in itself has under gone a rapid transformation after the inception of economic reforms in 1991. India's consent to the Agreement on Agriculture (AoA) also had a major impact leading to redefining of its agricultural trade. During this time span, various agricultural commodities exported from India have responded differently and their levels of comparative advantage in the global markets have altered significantly. Hence, it is imperative to have a systematic and well-structured analysis to find factors affecting alterations in the demand and supply functions of Indian agricultural commodities.

One of the outcome of the economic development of India has experienced in recent years is a marked change in the export pattern of its agricultural commodities. Several studies have shown export diversification of

Indian agricultural commodities such as tea, basmati rice, milk, meat, fruits, coffee, fish, processed food products, etc. Rapid urbanization, availability of a larger variety of agricultural commodities in the market, increased demand of commodities and growing processing facilities in the country are some of the predominant factors behind this shift. India's agricultural export performance is determined by a wide range of internal and external factors which affect the supply of and the demand for its agricultural exports. Domestic economic policies in general and trade policies in particular exercise a significant influence on our export performance. With recent government emphasis on export promotion of agricultural products, it has become important to know whether growth in rest of the world affects Indian exports and in what manner, how shifts in export prices affect its demand and supply and how production variations and pressure of Indian agricultural exports.

The demand and supply functions for selected agricultural commodities namely tea, coffee and basmati rice were estimated by using simultaneous equation system through two stage least squares model. Results are presented in table 4.15 & 4.16. Values of estimated coefficients along with their standard errors are shown in the table 4.15& 4.16. The coefficient of determination ($R^2$) is also presented in the table 4.15& 4.16, although its meaning in simultaneous model is at best ambiguous. The signs with the coefficients indicated the nature of relationship and significance of estimated coefficients were examined to choose a final demand and supply equation.

### 4.3.1 Demand function for selected commodities of Indian agricultural exports.

The results of demand function for export of tea, coffee and basmati rice have been presented in table 4.15. The structural equation has also been given showing the various factors affecting the demand function of export of selected agricultural commodities. The variables which affect the demand function of agricultural commodities are export price, world export price, world income level and the exports of last year.

**COFFEE:** Coffee is the traditionally exported commodity of India and contributed a major share in total agricultural exports from India. The analysis of export demand function of coffee explained that it was the export price and world price variables which affected the export demand of coffee significantly. Export price is included to show the variability in the demand of Indian coffee by the other importer countries whereas world price level is an important indicator of competition in international market included to analyze the impact of other exporter countries of coffee other than India in the world. The estimates of coefficient for coffee shown in the Table 4.15 explained that export price of coffee had a unexpected positive significant relationship with the export demand of coffee whereas world export price also had an unexpected negative significant relationship with the export demand of coffee. So it can be concluded that there were some variables other than our assumed variables which impacted export demand of Indian coffee significantly.

**TEA:** Tea is also one of the major exporting commodities of India having a major share in India's total agricultural exports. About 203.86 million kg tea is exported from India which brings about US $ 413 million as foreign exchange for the country per annum. Tea industry is a crucial source of revenue for the country. Being a labour intensive industry, it plays a vital role in employment generation also. Various variables were analyzed which could affect the export demand of tea. According to law of demand, demand is inversely related to price i.e. demand will rise if there is fall in price. Here also in our analysis export price had an expected significant negative relationship with the export demand of Indian tea during the study period i.e. 2001-11 as shown in the Table 4.15. This indicated that with decrease in export price export demand for Indian tea increased significantly. Whereas other variables included in the estimation of demand function of Indian tea didn't significantly affect the export demand. This showed that it was the export price which played a major role in the determination of export demand of Indian tea. So for increasing the export of tea major emphasis should be on keeping the export price of tea in check. This can be done by trying to economise the production as well as marketing process of tea export. For this purpose improving the position of Indian tea in the world market, tea board of India along with government of India had taken initiatives like tea act of 1953, etc.

**BASMATI RICE:** Basmati rice is also one of the major contributor in improving the position of India in world trade market. It contributed a major share in India's agricultural commodities export as during recent years export of non basmati rice was banned due to some quarantine measures so the whole emphasis was on the export of basmati rice to meet the increasing demand by the other nations. During the analysis it was analyzed that export price and world export price were the two variables which significantly affected the export demand of Indian basmati rice by the world. The various coefficients of variables were shown in table 4.15 which were assumed to affect the export demand of basmati rice in the analysis. The export price showed the expected significant negative relationship with the export demand of basmati rice. This indicated that with fall in the export price of basmati rice demand of Indian basmati rice increased in the world market which is in consent with the law of demand. Whereas the world price also showed the significant negative relationship with the export demand of basmati rice, which means that if the world price decrease then the export demand for Indian basmati rice will still increase. The reason for this may be the fact that India has stable long term trade partners in case of basmati rice exports and thus their demand decision may not be getting affected by short term changes in the prices of competitor countries.

**Structural equation**

$$Y_{1it} = a_{1i}Y_{3it} + a_{2i}X_{1it} + a_{3i}X_{2t} + a_{4i}X_{6it-1} + u_i$$

| Demand for $i^{th}$ product of Indian exports in thousand $ | Export Price variable in thousand $ / ton | World Export Price in thousand $/ ton | World Real Income in constant 2000 us$ | Lagged dependent Variable in thousand US$ | Stochastic term |
|---|---|---|---|---|---|

$Y_{1it}$ = Demand for Indian exports of $i^{th}$ commodity in $t^{th}$ year in thousand U.S. dollars.

$Y_{3it}$ = Export price of $i_{th}$ commodity in $t_{th}$ year in U.S.dollar per thousand metric tonnes.

$X_{1it}$ = World export price of $i^{th}$ commodity in $t^{th}$ year in U.S. dollar per thousand metric tonnes.

$X_{2it}$ = World real income in $t^{th}$ year at constant price.

$X_{6it-1}$ = Quantity of exports of $i^{th}$ commodity demanded in $(t-1)^{th}$ period in thousand U.S.dollars.

**Table 4.15: Estimated Demand function for the exports of Coffee, Tea and Basmati Rice 2001-2011: two stages least square model**

| Commodity | Estimates of Coefficient | | | | | |
|---|---|---|---|---|---|---|
| | intercept | $a_{1i}$ | $a_{2i}$ | $a_{3i}$ | $a_{4i}$ | $R^2$ |

| Coffee | 62571.86 (122898.4) | 48610.18** (54432.99) | - 1396.25** (3472.16) | 4.30E-8 (5.74E-8) | -0.13 (.879) | 0.23 |
|---|---|---|---|---|---|---|
| Tea | -132475 (219845.8) | - 191095.6** (206864.1) | 4755.785 (18506.84) | -1.8E-7 (2.05E-7) | 0.38 (1.86) | 0.50 |
| Basmati Rice | -283859 (868027.1) | - 663248.5** (499505.7) | -541447 ** (759223.6) | 6.32E-8 (7.67E-7) | 1.22.22 (0.18) | 0.94 |

*Note: * * significant at 5% level of significance.*

Figures in parenthesis show standard errors of regression coefficients.

**4.3.2 Supply function for selected commodities of Indian agricultural exports.**

The results showing the supply function were presented in table 4.16. Structural equation showing the various variables affecting the supply function was also given. Variables like export price, supply shock, domestic pressure and time variable were included in the structural equation.

**COFFEE:** the export supply of coffee was analysed by taking all the assumed variables but only one variable showed a significant impact on the export supply of coffee from India. The variable affecting the export supply was supply shock. The supply shock was included as the dummy variable in the analysis i.e. for positive fluctuations it was taken as one and for negative fluctuations it was taken as zero. The supply shock variable was positively and significantly related with the export supply of coffee as shown in the table 4.16. The positive supply shock indicated positive fluctuation of the production of coffee from trend i.e. production level had increased and had a significant positive impact on the export supply of coffee due to which there was improved export during the good crop years. No other variable was found significant in the supply function of coffee export. This means that coffee exports from India were most residual exports left after fulfilling the domestic consumption requirements in the country.

**TEA:** The results showed that the export supply of tea was significantly affected by the fluctuation in tea production and pressure of its demand pressure. The dummy variable i.e. supply shock showed a positive significant relationship with the export supply of Indian tea. Thus in the years of good crop and excess production due to favourable climatic conditions or improved production technologies, there was positive fluctuation in supply shock leading to increase in export supply of tea. One more variable also showed a significant but negative relationship with the export supply of tea from India namely demand pressure variable. Demand pressure variable was included to depict the impact of pressure of domestic consumption demand for tea on its export supply. This variable was negatively related to export supply as shown in the table 4.16 which indicated that the export supply increased with the fall in the demand pressure in the domestic exporting country. The export of tea was more in the years when pressure of domestic demand was less. The results suggested that there should be further improvement in the production of tea and demand pressure should be minimized further in order to improve the export supply of Indian tea and for further enhancement of Indian tea trade.

**BASMATI RICE:** Basmati Rice is a highly valued cash crop that earns substantial foreign exchange for India. Basmati rice export supply was too much affected by the export of non basmati rice as well as the export position of India during the previous years. During the study it was found that it was the lagged variable which was showing the positive significant relationship with the export supply of basmati rice. That means export of basmati rice was largely dependent on the export of that particular commodity during the previous year. The impact of other variables on export supply of basmati rice was not found significant. The lagged quantity of exports was the major influencing factor as shown in the table 4.16. Thus it may be concluded that the export supply of Indian basmati rice is on the basis of long term contracts with the importing countries.

**Structural equation**

| $Y_{2it}$ = $b_{1i}Y_{3it}$ + $b_{2i}X_{1it}$ + $b_{3i}X_{2t}$ + $b_{4i}X_{7it-1}$ + $e_{2i}$ | | | | | |
|---|---|---|---|---|---|
| Supply for $i^{th}$ product of Indian exports in thousand \$ | Export Price variable in thousand \$ / ton | Supply shock (dummy variable) | Demand pressure (Dummy Variable) | Lagged Variable (thousand US \$) | Stochastic term |

$Y_{2it}$ = Supply of Indian exports of $i^{th}$ commodity in $t^{th}$ year in thousand U.S. dollars

$Y_{3it}$ = Export price of $i_{th}$ commodity in $t_{th}$ year in U.S.dollar per thousand metric tonnes.

$X_{3it}$ = Supply shock in the $i^{th}$ commodity during $t^{th}$ year in thousand metric tonnes specified as dummy (one for positive fluctuation, zero for negative fluctuations)

$X_{4t}$ = Demand pressure in $t^{th}$ year at constant price.

$X_{7it-1}$ = Quantity of exports of $i^{th}$ commodity supplied in $(t-1)^{th}$ period in thousand U.S. dollars.

**Table 4.16:Estimated Supply function for the exports of Coffee, Tea and Basmati Rice 2001-2011: Two stages least square model**

| Commodity | Estimates of Coefficient | | | | | |
|---|---|---|---|---|---|---|
| | intercept | $b_{1i}$ | $b_{2i}$ | $b_{3i}$ | $b_{4i}$ | $R^2$ |
| Coffee | 35341.86 (185470.8) | -102575 (262863.2) | 3744.86** (84559.33) | 1.33E-7 (4.66E-7) | 0.85 (1.99) | 0.23 |
| Tea | 166954.9 (166144.3) | -147998 9103189.9 | 11709.64** (23321.84) | -1.59E-7** (7.82E-8) | 1.13 (0.51) | 0.85 |
| Basmati Rice | 409849.1 (961990.8) | -867850 (1466249) | 692244.9 (768349.6) | 8.60E-7 (9.64E-7) | 0.47** (.82) | 0.96 |

Note: * * *significant at 5% level of significance.*

Figures in parenthesis show standard errors of regression coefficients.

Agriculture is one of the strongholds of the Indian economy and it accounted for 13.9 per cent of the gross domestic product (GDP) in 2011-12. Agriculture draws its significance from the vital supply and demand links with other sectors of the economy and is a major source of livelihood for the rural population of India. More than 58 per cent of the country's population depends on agriculture for its livelihood. India is the largest producer of coconut, mango, banana, milk and milk products, cashew nut, pulses, ginger, turmeric and black pepper in the world. It is also the second largest producer of rice, wheat, sugar, cotton, fruits and vegetables. Agricultural production is likely to increase significantly.

India has a large and diverse agriculture and is one of the world's leading producers, but its presence on the world market has been modest in relation to the size of its agriculture. The total exports from India in 2010-11 were Rs.900471.00 crores and total agricultural products exports were Rs.120185.95 crores which contributed 10.47 per cent share in total export from India during 2010-11(Ministry of Agriculture). It indicated that India is a leading exporter of agricultural products. The Government's special efforts to encourage export of food grains in recent years through grant of World Trade Organization or WTO compatible subsidies has led to India becoming one of the leading exporters of food grains in the international market.

Agriculture exports have assumed greater significance today than before because of the open market policies adopted by the government after WTO agreement. Indian agriculture now is more connected to world agriculture and any disturbances in production, prices or trade in agriculture commodities at one point instantly have an impact throughout the world market. India has only less than one per cent share of world market in agricultural exports. External environment problems do affect our exports but internal pricing strategies as well as non price factors also erode our competitiveness. Export earnings are dependent not only on domestic production and distribution situation but also on many external factors like export prices, countries competing in product trade, international consumer's product preferences and many other socio political factors. Due to high volatility of international prices, analysis of domestic and international prices is required to be undertaken from time to time.

Further, most of our studies analyse agricultural exports at an aggregate level. So, it is difficult to draw easy interpretation and straight policy implications. Therefore, it is worthwhile to study export behaviour of individual agricultural commodities and the factors influencing their demand and supply.

There is a need to study each and every commodity individually as, it will depict problem faced in exporting that particular commodity to the other countries. In this study three agricultural commodities viz. tea, coffee and basmati rice have been selected which are imported export commodities from India and together contributed a major percentage share in agricultural exports from India. Tea and coffee were our traditional export commodities and there was wide variation overtime among the export of these commodities whereas Basmati Rice showed a continuous increase in the export. So, it needs the attention of the researcher to study them individually.

## 5.1   OBJECTIVES OF THE STUDY:

Keeping in view the above consideration research study entitled *"Estimation of Demand and Supply Functions for Export of Selected Agricultural Commodities from India"* was planned with specific objectives as under:

(1)   To study the growth rate and instability of exports of tea, coffee and basmati rice from India.

(2)   To analyse the destination wise pattern of exports of tea, coffee and basmati rice.

(3)   To estimate export demand and supply functions for tea, coffee and basmati rice.

## 5.2   RESEARCH METHODOLOGY:

Agriculture is the dominant sector of Indian economy, which determines the growth and sustainability of the economy. The present study attempts to look into various aspects of performance of agricultural exports of India. Indian agriculture is benefitting hugely from rising external demand and the sector's wider participation in the global economy. Thus looking to the importance of the present study and its objectives regarding with the agricultural exports, we have considered time series data of agricultural commodity's exports from the period 1990-91 to 2010-11.For the research purpose three commodities namely tea, coffee and basmati rice were selected. It is very important to study each commodity individually as, it will depict problem faced in exporting that particular commodity to the other countries. For estimation of trend, growth and instability various production functions were fitted and measures like compound growth rate, coefficient of variation and deviation from trend were estimated and for analyzing the pattern of export tabular analysis along with pie diagram was done.

Present study attempted to estimate Demand and Supply Functions for Export of Selected Agricultural Commodities from India. The demand and supply functions was estimated for coffee, tea and basmati rice using simultaneous equation model through two stage least square method.

The secondary data regarding quantity, value and unit value of export data of agricultural products overtime were collected from various publications and websites of Ministry of Agriculture, Govt. of India, Director General of commercial Intelligence & Statistics, Ministry of Commerce, Kolkata., Ministry of Consumer Affairs, Food & Public Distribution, Govt. of India, Govt. of India and Central Statistical Organization (CSO), compiled by Indiastat, Trademap, RBI, world economic outlook, Agriculture statistics of India, world development indicators.

## 5.3    RESULTS:

During the research it was analyzed that there were significant changes in the export quantity and value of different commodities. Export of coffee, tea and basmati rice was taken into consideration during the study. As these commodities were the most important contributor to India's total agricultural exports. Tea and coffee were the traditional export commodities of the nation whereas basmati rice was the commodity which was showing significant increase in it's share in the total agricultural export from India. That is why these three commodities were selected for the study. The results of the three objectives were presented as follows.

## 5.3.1 GROWTH    RATE    ANALYSIS    AND    INSTABILITY    IN AGRICULTURAL EXPORTS.

For the estimation of the export performance of the commodities growth rate and instability was analyzed. Growth rate analysis was used to measure the per year compound growth of export of selected commodities. Whereas the instability analysis was done to analyze the variation in the flow of particular commodity from the nation to the outside world and also helped to estimate the degree of variability in that particular commodity export. Trend analsis was also done for these three commodities to assess the trend in export quantity and value of selected agricultural commodities for the period from 1990 to 2011, models like linear, logarithmic, inverse, quadratic, cubic, compound, power, S model, growth and exponential model, etc. were tried and the best fit trend model was identified.

## GROWTH RATE ANALYSIS:

Growth rate analysis was done with the help of exponential production function. Compound annual growth rate was analyzed with the help of exponential equation and it was shown that among all the three commodities basmati rice has shown highest growth rate in terms of export quantity and value both. Whereas the compound annual growth rate of tea and coffee was less.

The compound annual growth rate for export of coffee in value terms was 4.29% per annum as compared to the compound annual growth rate of export quantity of coffee which was 2.76% per annum during the whole study period i.e. 1990-2011. This showed that the growth rate in export value of coffee was twice the growth rate in the export quantity of coffee. This showed that the price of coffee export are growing at a higher rate than the quantity of exports.

Similarly export of tea also showed 2.04% per annum growth in the export value as compared to the 1.37% per annum growth in the export quantity of tea which again showed that there was twice the increase in the growth of export value of tea as against the export quantity of tea.

Basmati rice the important export commodity of India showed highest growth rate during the study period. The compound annual growth rate for the export quantity of basmati rice was 11.14% per annum whereas for the export value of basmati rice it was 12.97% per annum for the study period 1990-2011. This showed that basmati rice is a prospective export commodity from India increasing it's share in total agricultural exports from India.

## INSTABILITY ANALYSIS:

In order to study the variability in the export trade of Agricultural commodities of India, an attempt was made to analyse the instability in exports of agricultural commodities over the period 1990-91 to 2010-11. The instability analysis was done with the help of two measures i.e. deviation from the trend analysis and coefficient of variation indicated as $I_1$ and $I_2$.

## A. COFFEE:

The deviation from the trend with respect to export quantity of coffee was 23.05% whereas the coefficient of variation was 15.73% during the years 1990-2011. This shows that export quantity of coffee was showing variability in the range of 15% to 23% as estimated by both the measures whereas the export value of coffee showed 50.52% deviation from the trend and 41.20% coefficient of variation in the export value of coffee. This showed that coffee export value showed higher instability during the study years i.e. 1990-2011.

## B. TEA:

Tea served as the stable exported commodity from India to the world as both the measures showed lesser instability. The export quantity of tea represented 19.95% deviation from the trend and 16.87% coefficient of variation during the study period 1990-2011. Both the measures represented instability less than 30% showing that export of tea was stable and acceptable. Whereas export value of tea showed 31.53% deviation from the trend and 28.29% coefficient of variation during the years 1990-2011. Although deviation from the trend was slight more than 30% but still the commodity was stable and less variable.

## C. BASMATI RICE:

Among all the cereals basmati rice gained the significant position in the export during the recent years. So its variability and instability measures were very important to be examined. Export quantity of basmati rice showed 77.46% of variation as deviation from trend and 182.80% as coefficient of variation whereas the export value of basmati rice also represented 106.43% as deviation from the trend and 281.09% coefficient of variation during the whole study period. This indicated the higher instability in the overall export of basmati rice from. This might be due to the wide range of export of basmati rice since 1990.

## 5.3.2 DESTINATION WISE PATTERN OF EXPORT

For the development of any nation it's foreign trade must be sound enough to develop the nation. the destination wise pattern of export of these selected commodities was analyzed in order to know the major destinations of export of these commodities as well as changes in destination over time. It was found during the study that various nations played different role some nations served as the promising partners and some served as only the small contributors.

**COFFEE:** Italy, Germany, Jordan, France, etc. served as the major importers of coffee from India. Italy maintained its position throughout the years 2001-2011. Whereas other nations like Spain, Switzerland, Crotia, etc. emerged as the major importers of coffee but Italy remained as the promising importing country of Indian coffee.

**TEA:** Tea is one of our major traditional export commodity of India. The major importers of Indian tea are Russian Federation, U.A.E., United Kingdom, Iraq, Kazakhstan, U.S.A., Iran, Germany, Pakistan and Australia. Russian Federation, U.A.E. and United Kingdom were top three export destinations of Indian tea throughout the study period. Russian federation served as the leading importer of tea from India and maintained it's position as leading importer till 2010. But during 2011 Tunisia emerged as the leading importer of the tea from India.

**BASMATI RICE:** The export of basmati rice had increased significantly since 2001. During the study period (2001-11) the major importing countries of Indian basmati rice were Saudi Arabia, United Arab Emirates, Iran, Kuwait, United States of America, Yemen, Belgium, Canada and Netherland. Saudi Arabia remained as the leading importer of Indian Basmati rice since 2001 and maintained its position till the end of the study period. It is clear that India had a consolidated market for its basmati rice exports. It had consistent long term trading partners during the whole study period. Some diversifications in the basmati rice export market for India was seen after 2005 in the form of inclusion of new countries as importers.

### 5.3.3 DEMAND AND SUPPLY FUNCTION OF SELECTED COMMODITIES OF INDIAN AGRICULTURAL EXPORTS

Export price variable has a significant negative relationship with demand for Indian exports of tea and basmati rice. world export price level has a significant positive relationship with the demand of basmati rice and coffee. This shows that world competition affects the demand for commodity significantly.

Export supply of coffee and tea was significantly affected by positive supply shocks. This means that export of these commodities was more in the years of higher production and low in the years of lower production. Export supply of tea was significantly affected by the negative demand pressure variable thus export of tea was more in the years when pressure of domestic demand was less. The supply of basmati rice export is affected significantly by it's last years export (lagged supply variable). Thus export supply of Indian basmati rice on the basis of long term contracts with the importing nation.

## 5.4    CONCLUSIONS:

1) Among three selected commodities basmati rice had a highest annual compound growth rate as compared to tea and coffee.

2) Basmati rice also showed highest instability in both quantity as well as in value terms as compared to other two commodities.

3) Saudi Arabia, Kuwait and U.A.E served as stable importing countries of basmati rice from India whereas Italy, Germany, Belgium and U.S.A. served as top most importing countries of coffee during the study period. Saudi Arabia and Italy remained the major importers of basmati rice and coffee respectively with the contribution of more than 40% share on an average during the whole study period.

4) Russian federation, U.A.E. and U.K. remained as leading importers of tea from India but during 2011 Tunisia emerged as top most importer country of tea from India.

5) Export Price variable had a significant negative relationship with demand for Indian exports of tea and basmati rice.

6) World export price level had a significant positive relationship with demand of basmati rice and coffee. This showed that world competition effects the demand for these commodities significantly.

7) Export supply of coffee and tea was significantly affected by positive supply shocks. Thus export of these commodities was more in years of higher production and lower in years of lower production.

8) Export supply of tea was significantly affected by negative demand pressure variable. Thus export of tea was more in years when pressure of domestic demand was less.

9) The supply of basmati rice exports was effected significantly by its last years export (lagged supply variable). Thus export supply of Indian basmati rice is on the basis of long term contracts with the importing countries.

## 5.5    POLICY IMPLICATION:

The policy implications emerging out of the study are outlined below in brief.

➤ India has some countries as stable business partners in export of these three commodities. It should try to maintain its stable contracts as well as try to tap new markets for its export.

➤ To counter the competition prevailing in world market good quality standards and consumer oriented approach is required.

➤ Policies aiming at reducing yield risk in coffee and tea production will be helpful in increasing the export supply of these commodities.

➢ Agrawal, P. C. and Hashim, S. R. 1990. Oilseeds in India - perspectives for 2001 A.D. *Oilseeds in India - perspectives for 2001 A.D.* **14**(1): 346.

➢ Aksoy, M.A. and Beghin, J.C. 2005. Global Agricultural Trade and Developing Countries. Manas Publications. New Delhi.

➢ Angles, S., Sundar, A. and Chinnadurai, M. 2011. Impact of globalization on production and export of turmeric in India - an economic analysis. *Agricultural Economics Research Review.* **24**(2): 301-308.

➢ Athukorala, P. 1991. An analysis of demand and supply factors in agricultural exports from developing Asian countries. *Weltwirtschaftliches Archiv.* **127**(4): 764-791.

➢ Athukorala, P. (1991). An Analysis of Demand and Supply Factors in Agricultural Exports from Developing Asian Countries, Review of World Economics. **127**(4):764-91

➢ Bera, B. K., Chakraborty, A. J., Nandi, A. K. and Sarkar, A. 2011. Growth and instability of food grains production of India and West Bengal. *Journal of Crop and Weed.* **7**(1): 94-100.

➢ Bordoloi, P. K. and Kakaty, S. C. 2003. Variations in production, export and domestic consumption of tea: an econometric study. *Economic Affairs (Calcutta).* **48**(2): 115-120.

➢ Chadha, G. K. 2007. Changing structure of demand for agricultural commodities:                    preparing for the future. *Indian Journal of Agricultural Marketing.* **21**(1): 1-42.

➢ Chand, K., Mathur, V. C. and Kumar, S. 2011. Temporal changes, growth and instability in the exports of agricultural commodities from 1962 to 1994. *Indian Jouurnal of Agriculture Research.* **35**(1): 25-30.

➢ Chaudhari, D. J. and Pawar, N. D. 2010. Growth, instability and price analysis of pigeonpea (Cajanus cajan L.) in Marathwada region. *Agriculture Update.* **5**(1/2): 158-162.

➢ Chern, W. S. and Yu, S. 2003. China's agricultural export and import behavior (Chinese Economy Series). *Agricultural trade and policy in China: issues, analysis and implications.* 185-203.

➢ Dahiya, P., Malik, D. P. and Singh, I. J. 2001. Trend and Growth Rate of Area, Production and Yield of Crops in Haryana. *The Bihar Journal of Agricultural Marketing.* **9**(2):13-26.

➢ Dellal, I. and Koc, A. A. 2003. An econometric analysis of apricot supply and export demand in Turkey. *Turkish Journal of Agriculture and Forestry.* **27**(5): 313-321.

➢ Deshmukh, M. S. 2010. Export competitiveness of horticultural sector in India- a commodity wise analysis. *Agricultural Situation in India.* **67**(1): 17-21.

➢ Devarajaiah, M. K. and Nataraju, M. S. 2010. Trends in export of rice from India. *Journal of Maharashtra Agricultural Universities.* **35**(2): 269-274.

➢ Hyma, J., Malik, D. P. and Hooda, B. K. 2003. A study on export performance of onion and potato from India. *Indian Journal of Agricultural Marketing.* **17**(3): 131-141.

➢ Indira, M. 1995. An analysis of coffee marketing under regulatory regime. *Indian Journal of Agricultural Marketing.* Special issue. 111-120.

➢ Kaur, A., Bansal, U. K., Saini, R. G. and Saini, S. 2004. A study about the export of turmeric; its status and prospects. *Indian Journal of Agriculture Economics.* **7**(4): 7-16.

➢ Kaur, Jasvindar And Rangi, P. S. 2000. Growth performance of oilseeds in India- an interstate analysis. *Agricultural Marketing.* **43**53(1): 5-12.

➢ Khem Chand, Mathur, V. C. and Kumar, S. 2001. An economic inquiry into growth and instability of India's agricultural exports. *Indian Journal of Agricultural Research.* **35**(1): 25-30.

➢ Kumar, C. N. and Muraleedharan, V. R. 2007. SPS regulations and competitiveness: an analysis of Indian spice exports. *South Asia Economic Journal.* **8**(2): 335-346.

➢ Kumar, P., Kumar, A., Parappurathu, S. and Raju, S. S. 2011. Estimation of demand elasticity for food commodities in India.*Agricultural Economics Research Review.* **24**(1): 1-14.

➢ Mathur, K.C. and Kumar, V.C. 2001. An economic inquiry into growth and instability of India's agricultural exports. *Indian Journal of Agricultural Research.* **35**(1): 25-30.

➢ Matos, M. A., Ninaut, E. S., Martins and F. de A. Z. Caiado, R. C. 2008. Analysis of the direct exports of Brazilian cooperatives. *Revista de Politica Agricola.* **17**(3): 75-87.

➢ Mendhe, N. P. and Degaonkar, A. M. 2010. Export performance of Indian chilli. *International Journal of Commerce and Business Management.* **3**(2): 252-257.

➢ Misra, V. N. and Rao, M. G. 2003. Trade policy, agricultural growth and rural poor: Indian experience, 1978-79 to 1999-2000. *Economic and Political Weekly*. **38**(43): 4588-4603.

➢ Mohanakumar, S. 2008. Sources of instability in natural rubber price: an analysis in the post-reform phase. *Journal of Plantation Crops*. **36**(3): 517-523.

➢ Murthy, S. D. and Subrahmanyam, K. V. 1999. Growth and instability in export of onion from India. *Indian Journal of Agricultural Marketing*. **13**(3): 21-27.

➢ Nawadkar, D. S. and Birari, K. S. 2000. Assessment of India's share in production and export of Fruits and Vegetables. *Indian journal of Agricultural Marketing*. 109-114.

➢ Niemi, J. 2003. Cointegration and error correction modelling of agricultural commodity trade: the case of ASEAN agricultural exports to the EU. *Agricultural and Food Science in Finland*. **12**(1): 1-113.

➢ Pal, G. 2010. Growth and instability in production and export of Indian lac. *Indian Forester*. **136**(9): 1235-1240.

➢ Paramjit N. and Raikhy, P.S. 2003. India's agricultural exports in the post-liberalisation period: problems and prospects. *Globalisation and agricultural crisis in India*. Book chapter. 204-219.

➢ Purbia, S. 2002. Production and trade instability in cashew - an economic analysis. *Indian Journal of Managemant*. **5**(1): 16-26.

➢ Raikhy, P. S. 2003. India's agricultural exports in the post- liberalisation period: problems and prospects. *Globalisation and agricultural crisis in India*. **5**(4): 204-219.

➢ Raju, K. V. 1990. An economic analysis of cultivation and export of coriander. *Agricultural Situation in India*. **45**(8): 523-526.

➢ Rangi, P. S. and Sidhu, M. S. 2001. A study on export of basmati rice from India. *Agricultural Marketing*. **43**(4): 13-20.

➢ Roy, S. S. 2011. Behavior of India's horticultural exports: does price competitiveness play a determining role. *Indian Journal of Agricultural Economics*. **66**(2): 230-240.

➢ Sadavati, S. 2006. A study on export of basmati rice. *Indian Journal of Agricultural Marketing*. **1**(2): 1066-2249.

➢ Sandhu, H. K. 1993. India's export share of black pepper in the world trade - An econometric analysis. *Indian Economic Journal*. **40**(3): 113-118.

➢ Sedaghat, R., Prakash, S. S. and Achoth, L. 2008. Study of structural changes in trade directions of Pistachio from Iran. *Mysore Journal of Agricultural Sciences.* **42**(3): 510-514.

➢ Sharma, H. R. and Sharma, R. K. 2003. Production and export performance of Indian tea - a temporal and cross-sectional analysis. *Agricultural Economics Research Review.* **16**(2): 152-170.

➢ Silva, C. R. L. and Da Carvalho, M. A. de. 2004. Destination of Brazilian agricultural exports. [Portuguese] *Informacoes Economicas - Instituto de Economia Agricola.* **34**(3): 26-40.

➢ Singh, A. J. and Singh, R. P. 1991. Growth performance of Punjab agriculture- an inter district analysis. *Agriculture Situation in India.* **66**(9):655-666.

➢ Singh, G and Chandra, H. 2001. The Paradox of declining agricultural output growth co-existing with declining prices of agricultural commodities. *Agriculture Situation in India.* **58**(5):187-203.

➢ Singh, K. K. and Shukla, H. L. 2010. Export performance and potential of mango in mango export zone Lucknow (UP). *Progressive Agriculture.* **10**(1): 188-191.

➢ Sujata, A., Singh, Kailash and Shukla, H. L. 2003. A study about export scenario of mangoes from India. *Indian Journal of Horticulture.* **67**: 1-8

➢ Sundaravaradarajan, K. R. and Kumar, K. R. R. 2002. Production and trade instability in cashew - an economic analysis. *Cashew.* **16**(1): 18-22.

➢ Tejaswi, P. B., Naik, B. K., Kunnal, L. B. and Basavaraj, H. 2006. Direction of trade and changing pattern of Indian coffee exports - an application of Markov chain analysis. *Karnataka Journal of Agricultural Sciences.* **19**(1): 71-75.

➢ Thomas, S. and Sheikh, W. 2012. Growth and composition of Indian agricultural exports during reform era. *Commerce and Management.* **1**(6): 92-104.

➢ Torquato, S. A. and Perez, L. H. 2006. Brazilian alcohol exports over 1996 to July 2005. *Informacoes Economicas - Instituto de Economia Agricola.* **36**(3): 18-32.

➢ Veena, U. M., Suryaprakash, S. and Achoth, L. 1994. Factors affecting export demand elasticity for Indian coffee. *Indian Coffee.* **58**(10): 11-12.

➢ Velavan, C. 2004. Performance of cashew: a growth rate analysis. *Cashew.* **18**(3): 27-31.

## LIST OF TABLES AND FIGURES

**Table 4.12:** Ranking of ten Major Importing countries of Coffee from India(2001-11)   (metric tons)

| Year / Importer | 2001 | 2002 | 2003 | 2004 | 2005 | 2006 | 2007 | 2008 | 2009 | 2010 | 2011 |
|---|---|---|---|---|---|---|---|---|---|---|---|
| Italy | 1st (37422) | 1st (41530) | 1st (45879) | 1st (42894) | 1st (52377) | 1st (62677) | 1st (49815) | 1st (52963) | 1st (43893) | 1st (48253) | 1st (64401) |
| Germany | 2nd (28546) | 2nd (27590) | 2nd (22347) | 2nd (19422) | 2nd (17234) | 2nd (26109) | 2nd (11279) | 2nd (15980) | 2nd (9635) | 2nd (18462) | 2nd (37769) |
| Belgium | 3rd (15253) | 3rd (15881) | 3rd (17798) | 3rd (11676) | 4th (9201) | 3rd (14744) | 3rd (9978) | 3rd (11511) | 3rd (7941) | 3rd (10122) | 3rd (21508) |
| United States of America | 4th (13076) | 6th (5279) | | 6th (5889) | | | | | | | |
| Spain | 5th (11784) | 4th (10593) | 4th (12355) | 4th (11140) | 3rd (10322) | 4th (11250) | 4th (8549) | 4th (8582) | 4th (6873) | 5th (4860) | 4th (13125) |
| Switzerland | 6th (7630) | | 9th (3403) | | | | | | 10th (3275) | | |
| Slovenia | 7th (5860) | 5th (6473) | 5th (7146) | 5th (7766) | 5th (8400) | 5th (7152) | 6th (5445) | 8th (4429) | 7th (3851) | 10th (2713) | 6th (6843) |
| Greece | 8th (4670) | 9th (4671) | 8th (3734) | 8th (5134) | 7th (4786) | 7th (5674) | 5th (5572) | 6th (4764) | 5th (4707) | | 7th (6417) |
| Russian Federation | 9th (4473) | 10th (4393) | | 7th (5654) | 6th (7887) | 10th (3723) | 10th (3264) | | | | |
| Netherlands | 10th (4056) | 8th (4884) | 10th (3403) | | | | | | | | |
| Japan | | 7th (5173) | 7th (5119) | 9th (4660) | 8th (4333) | 6th (6135) | | | | | |
| France | | | 6th | 10th | 9th | 8th | 9th | | | | |

| | | | | | | | | | |
|---|---|---|---|---|---|---|---|---|---|
| e | (5568) | (3680) | (4280) | (4090) | (3328) | | | | |
| Portugal | | | 10th (4104) | | | | | | |
| Algeria | | | | 9th (3865) | | | | | 8th (5716) |
| Crotia | | | | | 7th (4688) | 5th (5605) | 8th (3832) | 8th (3087) | |
| Jordan | | | | | 8th (3937) | 7th (4476) | 6th (4394) | 4th (6332) | 5th (7177) |
| Australia | | | | | | 9th (3298) | | 7th (3403) | 9th (4524) |
| Kuwait | | | | | | 10th (3787) | | 6th (4116) | |
| Egypt | | | | | | | 9th (3307) | | |
| Israel | | | | | | | | 9th (2981) | |
| Saudi Arabia | | | | | | | | | 10th (4234) |

Table 4.13: Ranking of ten Major Importing countries of Tea from India (2001-11)
(metric tones)

| Year / Importer | 2001 | 2002 | 2003 | 2004 | 2005 | 2006 | 2007 | 2008 | 2009 | 2010 | 2011 |
|---|---|---|---|---|---|---|---|---|---|---|---|
| Russian Federation | $1^{st}$ (67007) | $1^{st}$ (41930) | $1^{st}$ (40559) | $1^{st}$ (31882) | $1^{st}$ (28963) | $1^{st}$ (32477) | $1^{st}$ (30711) | $1^{st}$ (33546) | $1^{st}$ (37818) | $1^{st}$ (38092) | $2^{nd}$ (46443) |
| United Arab Emirates | $2^{nd}$ (21917) | $3^{rd}$ (22257) | $2^{nd}$ (23085) | $2^{nd}$ (27460) | $2^{nd}$ (27204) | $3^{rd}$ (18116) | $2^{nd}$ (26467) | $3^{rd}$ (25034) | $2^{nd}$ (22764) | $4^{th}$ (21698) | $5^{th}$ (22285) |
| United Kingdom | $3^{rd}$ (20692) | $4^{th}$ (21842) | $3^{rd}$ (19521) | $3^{rd}$ (20875) | $3^{rd}$ (24093) | $2^{nd}$ (26618) | $3^{rd}$ (24883) | $2^{nd}$ (27722) | $3^{rd}$ (22540) | $3^{rd}$ (22340) | $3^{rd}$ (31395) |
| Iraq | $4^{th}$ (16711) | $2^{nd}$ (36715) | $5^{th}$ (11145) | $5^{th}$ (10625) | $4^{th}$ (16234) | $7^{th}$ (9027) | | | $6^{th}$ (10733) | | |
| Kazakhstan | $5^{th}$ (137422) | $5^{th}$ (6585) | $4^{th}$ (11916) | $4^{th}$ (15717) | $5^{th}$ (11016) | $9^{th}$ (5578) | | $6^{th}$ (7854) | $9^{th}$ (7732) | $5^{th}$ (15260) | $6^{th}$ (16652) |
| Poland | $6^{th}$ (9259) | $7^{th}$ (5709) | $9^{th}$ (4389) | $9^{th}$ (4200) | | | | | | | |
| United States of America | $7^{th}$ (8875) | $6^{th}$ (6314) | $6^{th}$ (8472) | $6^{th}$ (8286) | $6^{th}$ (8892) | $5^{th}$ (9387) | $5^{th}$ (10457) | $5^{th}$ (11774) | $4^{th}$ (11999) | $6^{th}$ (15186) | $7^{th}$ (16222) |
| Iran (Islamic Republic of) | $8^{th}$ (6985) | | | $7^{th}$ (7686) | $7^{th}$ (7950) | $6^{th}$ (9298) | $4^{th}$ (13792) | $4^{th}$ (16676) | $5^{th}$ (11154) | $2^{nd}$ (22681) | $8^{th}$ (14639) |
| Germany | $9^{th}$ (5931) | $8^{th}$ (5333) | $7^{th}$ (5651) | $8^{th}$ (5770) | $9^{th}$ (5769) | | $8^{th}$ (6402) | | | $7^{th}$ (10173) | |
| Japan | $10^{th}$ (4432) | | | | | | | | | | |
| Sudan | | $9^{th}$ (3312) | | | | | | | | | |
| Pakistan | | $10^{th}$ (3090) | $8^{th}$ (5450) | | $8^{th}$ (6860) | $4^{th}$ (12837) | | $8^{th}$ (7736) | $8^{th}$ (8045) | $8^{th}$ (8174) | $4^{th}$ (24870) |
| Australia | | | $10^{th}$ | | $10^{th}$ | | $6^{th}$ | $9^{th}$ | $10^{th}$ | $10^{th}$ | $9^{th}$ |

| | | | | | | | | | |
|---|---|---|---|---|---|---|---|---|---|
| a | (4278) | | (4773) | | (6559) | (6917) | (7028) | (7095) | (9092) |
| Kenya | | 10th (4108) | | | | | | | |
| Saudi Arabia | | | | 8th (5625) | 7th (6414) | 10th (6694) | | | 10th (7993) |
| Cambodia | | | | 10th (5357) | 9th (5470) | | | | |
| Srilanka | | | | | 10th (5441) | | | 9th (7106) | |
| Egypt | | | | | | 7th (7825) | | | |
| Afghanistan | | | | | | | 7th (8885) | | |
| Tunisia | | | | | | | | | 1st (67044) |

**Table :4.14 : Ranking of ten importing countries of Basmati Rice from India (2001-11)**
**(metric tons)**

| Year / Importer | 2001 | 2002 | 2003 | 2004 | 2005 | 2006 | 2007 | 2008 | 2009 | 2010 | 2011 |
|---|---|---|---|---|---|---|---|---|---|---|---|
| Saudi Arabia | 1st (4060 96.7) | 1st (3668 14.2) | 1st (4364 15.5) | 1st (6906 65.23) | 1st (6436 51.51) | 1st (4995 84.76) | 1st (5435 30.24) | 1st (5244 01.67) | 1st (6404 04.41) | 2nd (6227 04.96) | 2nd (7212 45.48) |
| Kuwait | 2nd (6525 7.26) | 3rd (6311 9.98) | 3rd (4886 2.93) | 3rd (9572 2.76) | 2nd (9133 5.38) | 2nd (1090 67.36) | 3rd (1130 66.57) | 4th (1115 47.25) | 4th (1394 73.57) | 4th (1975 90.4) | 4th (1998 69.77) |
| United Kingdom | 3rd (6351 4.44) | 2nd (7254 3.62) | 2nd (8584 8.31) | 2nd (9582 5.05) | 3rd (8471 5.37) | 4th (7141 1.67) | 4th (7137 7.56) | 5th (6256 3.1) | 6th (3696 6.43) | 5th (7738 4.45) | 6th (1416 66.21) |
| U.S.A. | 4th (2685 4.9) | 4th (3072 0.58) | 5th (2675 7.38) | 6th (2692 3.78) | 6th (3328 5.4) | 6th (3450 1.92) | 6th (3573 8.68) | 6th (3962 5.13) | 7th (2592 2.13) | 7th (4748 9.73) | 8th (9181 6.94) |
| U.A.E. | 5th (1528 6.11) | 5th (2743 5.49) | 4th (4025 6.89) | 4th (6188 2.22) | 4th (6210 0.45) | 3rd (3450 1.92) | 2nd (1931 02.03) | 2nd (4561 46.51) | 2nd (6161 25.13) | 1st (6347 69.33) | 1st (7288 23.29) |
| Yemen | 6th (1411 9.41) | 6th (1791 2.66) | 7th (1545 1.15) | 5th (3763 2.62) | 5th (5038 8.4) | 5th (4068 9.2) | 5th (4995 8.53) | 7th (3147 5.68) | 5th (6180 9.92) | 6th (7004 2.1) | 7th (9211 2.14) |
| France | 7th (9083 .5) | 7th (1310 6.7) | 8th (1202 7.65) | 8th (1634 0) | | | | | | | |
| Belgium | 8th (7194 .86) | 8th (1014 6.8) | 9th (1157 3.16) | 9th (1580 4) | 7th (3102 1) | 7th (2438 6.5) | 10th (1334 6.59) | | | | |
| Canada | 9th (7126 .27) | 10th (9032 .04) | | | 10th (1349 7.95) | 9th (1586 9.79) | 8th (1356 5.22) | 9th (1783 5.2) | 9th (9244. 81) | | |
| Germany | 10th (6051 .17) | | 10th (9161 .5) | 10th (1495 8.19) | | | | | | | |
| South africa | | 9th (9671 .85) | | | | | | | | | |
| Italy | | | 6th (1914 3.3) | 7th (1988 8.76) | 8th (2280 8.11) | | | | | | |
| Netherland | | | | | 9th (1840 5.97) | 8th (1885 0.61) | 7th (1785 1.68) | 10th (1114 7.3) | | 10th (2309 7.67) | 10th (3727 5) |

| | | | | | |
|---|---|---|---|---|---|
| Iran | 10th (15110.8) | | 3rd (170947.47) | 3rd (364602.51) | 3rd (450657.16) | 3rd (614922.16) |
| Qatar | | 9th (13430) | | | | |
| Oman | | | 8th (25119.61) | | | |
| Singapore | | | | 8th (9672) | | |
| Jordan | | | | 10th (9235.9) | 9th (25602.15) | 9th (52928.98) |
| Iraq | | | | | 8th (36907.9) | 5th (151961.25) |

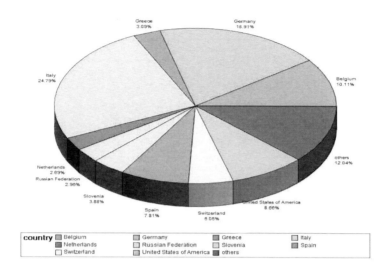

**Figure 4.10: Destination of India's Coffee Exports (2001)**

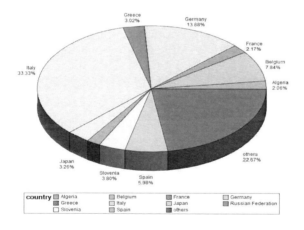

**Figure4.11: Destination of India's Coffee Exports (2006)**

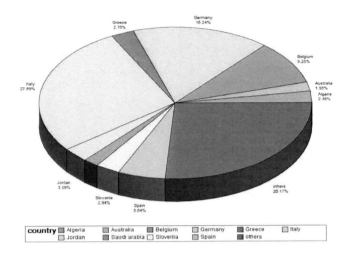

**Figure 4.12: Destination of India's Coffee Exports (2011)**

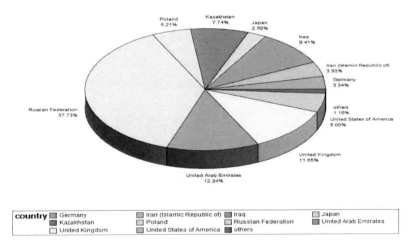

**Figure 4.13 : Destination of India's Tea Exports (2001)**

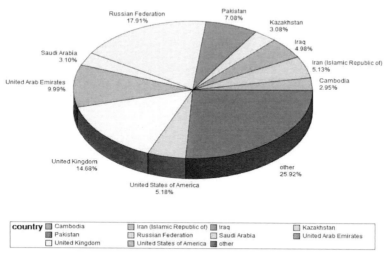

**Figure 4.14 :Destination of India's Tea Exports (2006)**

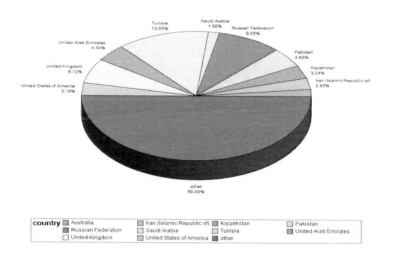

**Figure 4.15 : Destination of India's Tea Exports (2011)**

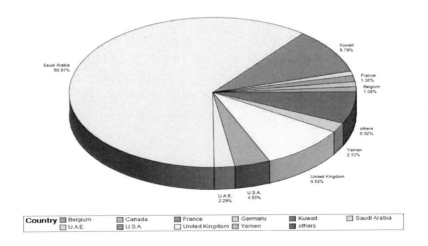

**Figure 4.16 : Destination of India's Basmati Rice Exports (2001)**

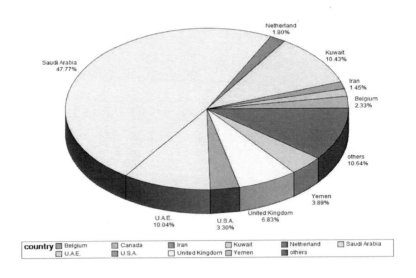

**Figure 4.17: Destination of India's Basmati Rice Exports (2006)**